THE BOC

Ravi Shankar Etteth is the editor of *The Sunday Standard*. He is the author of three previous novels, *The Tiger by the River*, *The Village of the Widows* and *The Gold of Their Regrets*, as well as a collection of short stories, *The Scream of the Dragonflies*. He lives in New Delhi.

THE BOOK OF SHIVA

RAVI SHANKAR ETTETH

First published in India in 2016 by Harper Element
An imprint of HarperCollins *Publishers*

Copyright © Ravi Shankar Etteth 2016

P-ISBN for paperback edition: 978-93-5177-698-7
P-ISBN for hardback edition: 978-93-5177-815-8
E-ISBN: 978-93-5177-699-4

2 4 6 8 10 9 7 5 3 1

For sale in the Indian subcontinent only

Ravi Shankar Etteth asserts the moral right
to be identified as the author of this work.

HarperCollins *Publishers*
A-75, Sector 57, Noida, Uttar Pradesh 201301, India
1 London Bridge Street, London, SE1 9GF, United Kingdom
Hazelton Lanes, 55 Avenue Road, Suite 2900, Toronto, Ontario M5R 3L2
and 1995 Markham Road, Scarborough, Ontario M1B 5M8, Canada
25 Ryde Road, Pymble, Sydney, NSW 2073, Australia
195 Broadway, New York, NY 10007, USA

Typeset in 11/14 Garamond Premier Pro Regular at
Manipal Digital Systems, Manipal

Printed and bound at
Replika Press Pvt. Ltd.

Salutations to

Lord Hanuman	The Goddess Kali
ancient father, warrior, the fount of wisdom and mercy who protects us all from darkness	*primordial mother, the giver of knowledge and sustenance, and the slayer of evil*

each of whom is from Shiva and is Shiva

The Monk Meets His Guru Who Asks for a Gift He Deserves

On the day the monk who would be named Asananda was to travel to the Himalayas to find the Book of Shiva, he overslept as usual. His guru, Gyanananda, allowed him to wake after dawn, unlike the other monks who had to rise before the brahmamuhurtham at four o'clock – the best time for meditation and worship. He had asked his master why he was allowed this indulgence.

'My son, you woke up a long time ago,' the guru answered. 'Only, you don't know it.'

The monk was tall and lean, with a deeply lined face. His eyes were small, but long with thick lashes, and reflected, simultaneously, the wariness and calm of an old soldier's gaze. His head was shaved close, giving it a blue sheen with a grey undertone. His chin was covered with salt-and-pepper stubble.

Years ago – he couldn't remember when – the monk had come to the ancient, holy town of Rishikesh after meditating in a Himalayan cave, outside which time fell like snow. The journey had taken him two months. He had made his way through fickle, ice-bound trails, treacherous glaciers and frozen streams to arrive at Kullu valley. From there, he had hitched a jeep ride to Mandi, a small town with colourful markets where men in embroidered caps sat on shop verandas and smoked hookahs. A few days later, he crossed Paonta Sahib, where, centuries ago, the great Sikh guru Gobind Singh had meditated in the forest before ascending to heaven on his beloved horse, Dilbagh.

It was noon when Asananda reached Rishikesh. He ambled through the sun-spotted shade of ancient trees, his shadow scraping the shadows of the old walls along the eastern riverbank. He carried a wooden staff to negotiate the narrow, steep hill roads. Over his shoulder was slung a cloth satchel that contained his meagre possessions. Rishikesh's two-kilometre length of temples, ashrams, ceremonial bathing ghats and shops that sold everything, from religious artefacts to vegetables, is situated on the banks of the Ganga. The area is called Swargashram.

Asananda was hungry. Following the scent of food, he reached an ashram whose gates were guarded by a gigantic blue statue of Lord Shiva wearing a leopard skin and holding a trident. The monk stepped inside, on to a sandy yard, cooled by the shade of trees. There, on a veranda, sat Guru Gyanananda, eating rice and vegetables off a copper plate. A large gathering of birds surrounded him, twittering and squawking. Some of them sat on his shoulders, heads cocked, gazing in concentration at the food on the plate. A brown mynah perched on the matted topknot of his thick, brown hair, while a crow hopped up close, looking at him sideways and cawing. Asananda watched the guru as he ate.

Occasionally, Gyanananda stopped to scatter rice grains on the ground over which the birds quarrelled noisily among themselves.

'Well?' The guru looked up.

'I was hoping for some food,' the monk replied.

Gyanananda's eyes twinkled mischievously. 'Really? Next, you'll be telling me you are hoping for shelter.'

The monk thought for a while. 'Perhaps,' he answered. 'I have come a long way, and I'm always hopeful when I set out in the morning.'

'Hopeful of what?'

'I don't hope for anything in particular, only that everything will turn out well. Like a lost child would be found by her parents or a speeding car wouldn't knock down an old woman crossing the road. Things like that.'

'Then I shall name you Asananda – the one who finds joy in hope,' the guru said. 'And you shall live here as long as you wish.'

The monk bowed his head, acknowledging the guru's offer.

'What can you give me as gurudakshina?' asked Gyanananda. 'A guru always asks a disciple for a gift before accepting him into an order.'

'Whatever I can give, master.'

Gyanananda closed his eyes and thought. 'Go and find me something I deserve,' he said. 'By that, I will know you.'

The monk felt his stomach protest. He hadn't eaten since the night before. It never bothered him earlier, when he used to go without food or water for days in the cave. But when he saw Gyanananda eating noisily and belching between mouthfuls of rice, the monk suddenly felt famished. As if sensing his hunger, the guru looked up and indicated with a nod that Asananda should leave. The monk picked up his belongings and left the guru to his meal.

He walked along the Ganga, its flow accompanying his thoughts. He crossed the gigantic, brightly painted gates of wealthy ashrams guarded by gaudy statues of gods, as well as impoverished ones with dilapidated walls that had begun losing the battle against the thick vines and wild grass reaching through their cracks. A white cow nosed through a heap of garbage by the roadside and the monk felt sad that he could not offer it food. A stray dog slumbered in the sun, its ribs showing through loose, scabby skin. It opened one eye as the monk passed, before growling and going back to sleep. The monk wondered what Gyanananda meant when he asked for something that he deserved. It could not have been money, since anyone could see that Asananda was a poor monk. It could not have been knowledge, since the master knew more than anyone else, or he would not be a master at all. It could certainly not be food, Asananda thought wryly, listening to his grumbling stomach.

He could smell hemp. A man in a patched white shirt and a shabby cloth cap was sitting on a crumbling stone bench on the roadside, smoking a clay pipe. A ramshackle wooden pushcart loaded with fruit – apples, oranges, bananas and a few guavas – was parked beside him. As the monk approached, the man greeted him and asked, 'Would you like a smoke? Or would you rather have a banana or an apple? You look like you could use one. You don't have to pay for it. Offering food to holy men will do my karma good.'

The monk declined the fruit-seller's offer and said he was not a holy man.

'I've never seen you in these parts before,' the fruit-seller observed.

The monk explained that he had been travelling for many days, all the way from the Himalayas, seeking a guru.

'Did you find one?'

'I found someone I like. But he won't take me in until I bring him something he deserves.'

'Ah, is that the gurudakshina he is asking for? Did he say what he wanted?'

Asananda shook his head.

'But how can a guru ask for a gift from an initiate without specifying what he wants? It sounds suspiciously like something Gyanananda would do,' the fruit-seller said.

The monk nodded dourly. 'You seem to know him well,' he said. 'What's he like?'

'I've met him only once. But I've heard from wandering yogis that people talk about him even in places as far away as Kedarnath and Badrinath, and even in Chitkul, the last village on the border.'

'Really? What do they say?'

'That's the mystery. They describe him as a great master, but none of them can explain how he became one before he founded Asashram.'

Gyanananda's ashram on the Ganga was called Asashram – the Dwelling of Hope. His followers were part of the Order of Hope.

The fruit-seller continued, 'One day I went to meet him with some fresh fruit from my little garden, but he turned me away. He asked me if I was done with whatever I was doing and said I should come to him only after I have finished.'

The monk grew curious. 'What were you doing that is so important?'

'Watering a tree,' said the fruit-seller.

'What tree?' the monk asked, his curiosity whetted.

The fruit-seller did not reply. He briefly closed his eyes. When he opened them, untold stories swirled within. He stood up and knocked the bowl of his pipe a few times on the side of the bench, shaking off the ash and bits of coal, before tucking it into a side pocket of his kurta.

'You say Gyanananda sent you out on this search?' the fruit-seller asked. Asananda nodded. The fruit-seller scrutinized his face, as if looking for signs of subterfuge. Seemingly satisfied with what he saw, he asked the monk to follow him, and strode up a narrow, unpaved path that climbed towards a copse of trees. The fruit-seller was wiry and tall, and walked with long, loping strides. Asananda had to struggle to keep up with him. Besides, the hunger was making him feel slightly dizzy. The discipline he had mastered in the Himalayas, where he had meditated on the great god Shiva without food or water for months, didn't seem to work in Rishikesh. The dun-coloured path narrowed as it entered the woods and then ascended the slope of the hill. The river's soothing mantra could be heard through the trees. The path ended at a massive, rusted iron gate, which hung precariously on a rotting frame set into a decaying stone wall. The fruit-seller courteously stood aside to let the monk pass.

Beyond the gate was an overgrown garden. It was chaotic with trees old and young: bamboo, ironwood and chestnut. Fruit trees fought against the determined onslaught of bushes. The air was redolent of oranges and guavas. Untamed vines encircled tree trunks, festive with bright wildflowers. Grass grew knee-high. The remnants of a wall snaked around the crest of the hill, disappearing in places among bamboo thickets and stunted mountain trees that looked carelessly pollarded. The garden was very large; it stretched over the entire scalp of the small hill. Asananda walked gingerly. He knew the bushes and grass could conceal ant holes that were several feet deep and into which a man could fall and be buried in mud. He looked around for his host who seemed to have disappeared into the bamboo thickets. He called out, and a faint voice answered, muffled by the sibilant rustle of bamboos and the distant gurgle of the river. It seemed to be an invitation to come further.

As he cleared the last thicket, Asananda halted in his tracks. The ruins of a gigantic mansion confronted him, its diseased façade standing proudly against the cloudless mountain sky. Its great balconies had crumbled along the moss-covered walls and looked as if they'd cantilevered to a stop on either side. The large doors, which once guarded the entrance, had rotted and fallen away, and the interior lay open to the elements. Through the yawning gap, a piece of glass winked like a demon's trick. The gap-toothed marble balustrade of the terrace was tainted with uneven black patches. The abandoned building looked as if a host of memories lingered in the gloom like the phantoms of long departed guests.

'Welcome home,' the fruit-seller said, spreading his arms wide.

'How did you find this place?' asked Asananda. In the mountains, there were many abandoned buildings that had fallen into ruin, either because the occupants had died without heirs or litigation over ownership continued unresolved for decades. Wanderers, beggars and vagrants took shelter under the broken rafters, keeping owls, bats and nesting ravens company.

'I was born in this house,' the fruit-seller said. 'It's a long story.'

'Tell me,' said Asananda, forgetting his hunger. He squatted on the broad marble steps that were veined blue. His companion gazed up at the towering wreck that spread its lengthening shadow in the dying afternoon like the approach of a ghost ship. His eyes were haunted by sadness tinged with pride.

The Monk and the Pomegranate Tree

'My name is Amogh,' the fruit-seller introduced himself, 'and this is the home of my ancestors.'

'It must have been magnificent once,' Asananda said.

'I live here,' answered the fruit-seller, in a defiant tone. 'I've had offers to sell which would make my old age fairly comfortable. Building contractors are buying up whole mountainsides, but I refuse to sell this house. A long time ago, something happened here and it changed everything for me.'

The wind rustled in the bamboo groves behind the house as if someone was moving quickly through the thickets. Asananda looked around the overgrown garden. A wasp, drunk on fruit juice, buzzed in a lazy circle and flew away. Amogh pointed towards a large, leafless pomegranate tree that stood on a small grassy knoll.

'My grandfather planted it, and my mother used to water it,' he said in a neutral tone, as if reciting from memory. 'When we were children, we used to accompany her to the tree every day, carrying little brass vessels filled with water.'

'We?'

'My little sister, Ketaki, and I,' the fruit-seller said with a little quiver in his voice.

'Where is she?'

'I don't know. But she was such a beautiful little girl,' he replied. 'Then she disappeared with the Canutha ruby and was never seen again.'

'What is the Canutha ruby?' Asananda asked. The fruit-seller squatted beside the monk and told him about his sister and the ruby.

Ketaki was a beautiful little girl. She had gleaming black hair, which her mother would plait and decorate with flowers picked from the garden. She had an oval face and large serious eyes that the maids lined with kohl every morning after her bath. She was as mischievous as a small monkey and could clamber up trees faster and higher than Amogh, reaching the topmost branch first and challenging him to match her skill.

The valley dozed, tucked in the gently undulating terrain of the Himalayan foothills – woolly with pines and crested with green fez. The mist smoked indolently over the mountaintops. The Ganga was a great golden girdle in the soft sun. The stately barges of rich merchants and aristocrats sailed alongside the smaller boats and ferry. Amogh's was an old family; his grandfather had been an important government official during the time the British ruled India. Amogh's father was passionate about precious stones. Over the years, he had become an expert, and was much in demand by those looking to test the provenance and quality of rare stones. The family owned a barge and a large launch that the father used to travel to Haridwar. From there, he would fly to Delhi or Bombay, sometimes accompanied by his wife, to meet some big diamond merchant or an impecunious raja who wanted to sell a precious stone. One day, upon returning home, he immediately went to his room, shutting the door behind him. The children knew he had come home with something special

– a rare gem that mystified him. This did not happen often, but when it did, the family knew the signs. Father would not emerge from his sanctuary for days; food had to be sent to him through a special dumbwaiter. Only Mother was allowed in, that too briefly, to pick up his dirty clothes and change the bed linen. At such times, the children were not allowed to make any noise. Not until their father emerged from his room, sporting a triumphant look; the black curl of hair, which Mother teasingly said gave him the Elvis look, pasted against his forehead, his dark eyes flashing with laughter.

On other occasions, Amogh and Ketaki would play noughts and crosses under the pomegranate tree, sitting on a red chequered cloth to keep the damp grass from wetting their clothes. Often Mother would bring a book and a cushion and lie down beside them and read. The book was always *Anna Karenina*. She would sob quietly each time she reached the part where the heroine confesses her affair to her husband Alexei Alexandrovich and, later, when Vronsky stops being in love with her. The children would stop their game and look at their mother with concern; but she would wipe her tears, smile and say, 'Go on, play children, it's only a story in a book.'

'Do stories make you cry, Mummy?' Ketaki once asked.

'Only the ones that touch your heart,' Mother replied.

'Why do they make you cry, Mummy?'

'Because any one of them could have been your story. And when the book ends, you are glad that they aren't.'

Sometimes Father would join them, a glass of beer in his hand and a Dunhill cigarette in the other. Ketaki would squeal with joy and run to him, plunging her little hands into his pockets. Tickled, Father would squirm and laugh, spilling beer on the grass. Finally, Ketaki would triumphantly withdraw her hand, clutching a diamond or a ruby that flashed magically in the sun. Amogh found the dazzle of a gem mesmerizing, as if a star was trapped within. Often, Father allowed Ketaki to play with the stones.

But one afternoon when she seized a shining red ruby from Father's pocket and ran to show it to Mother, he called out, 'Be careful, little Ketaki, it's the Canutha ruby.'

'I think I've heard of it,' Mother said, looking up from her book. 'Something about a curse?'

Father laughed, mussed Mother's hair, and sat down beside her on the soft green grass. He called out to a waiting servant for more beer. 'All famous stones like the Canutha ruby have some legend or the other about them, it only increases their value,' he said. 'The current prince of Canutha is broke. The ruby has been in his family for generations but he needs the money.'

Canutha was a small princely fiefdom in Rajasthan that had fallen into penury after India got Independence and the new government stopped supporting Indian royalty who had never worked for a day in their lives. Many of them had to sell their vintage cars, palaces and jewellery. Or convert their palaces into ramshackle hotels, peddling a royal welcome. The Canutha ruby was part of a famous tiara worn by a long-dead queen.

'What is the Canutha legend? It's something dreadful, I'm sure,' said Mother. Father took a thoughtful drag of his cigarette, releasing fragrant blue smoke into the clear mountain air. 'The ruby belonged to the lord of Canutha, whose palace lay at the foot of the Aravalli mountains,' he began after a long pull from the beer glass.

'It was believed that the blood-coloured stone was once embedded in the hood of Lord Shiva's serpent. The raja prayed for many years and was given the ruby by Shiva as a reward. The god told him that tragedy would not cross the threshold of any house where the ruby was worshipped, but would bring ruin to those who did not honour it. The stone was installed in the palace temple where, for many generations, the kings and the people of Canutha worshipped it. But when Babur, the first Mughal, conquered large parts of north India, Canutha was annexed and became a tiny part of his gigantic empire. The Canutha temple met the fate of other temples under the Mussalmans, who raided and destroyed it.

An Arab mercenary, who was part of Babur's army, gave the Canutha ruby to the king, who in turn gave it to one of his concubines. Within months, Babur lay dead in his palace in the ancient city of Agra. The concubine gave the stone as a gift to Babur's son, the lenient and generous Emperor Humayun, hoping for his protection. Humayun accepted the ruby, but soon lost his empire to invaders and had to flee to Persia on a long march with only forty men, eating the flesh of horses that had been boiled in the helmets of his soldiers. After many misfortunes, Humayun returned to India, only to die by tumbling down some stairs. Palace scribes recorded that he was holding the Canutha stone when he fell. His son, the emperor Akbar, who married a princess from Canutha, following the practice of taking Hindu wives in exchange for treaties with Hindu kings, gave the ruby to her family as part of the meher – the bride price. By then, the rulers of Canutha had forgotten the tradition of worshipping Shiva's stone. It lay among other precious stones in their treasury for generations, until the present prince put it up for sale to settle his debts.

'The Canutha legend goes that Shiva protects the ruby, and anyone who steals it is taken alive by Yama, the God of Death, to the nether realm, where he is doomed to live forever,' Father said with a careless laugh. 'I traced its origins and found it has indeed been mentioned in Mughal records that date back to the late fifteenth century, which was when Babur invaded India. In an 1898 British inventory of royal treasuries, it is referred to as a twenty-five-carat, forty-three-carat uncut, brilliant stone with a six-pointed star, mined from the Mogok mines belonging to the king of Canutha, and insured for 21,000 pounds.'

Mother shivered a little and crossed her arms. She looked towards where Ketaki was playing with the ruby, laughing and holding it out at the sun that shone through it to cast a red star on her face. It looked like a translucent spider, its belly filled with blood.

Mother turned to Father and said, 'You scare me by telling me this story sitting under our favourite tree. You know the Greek legend of the pomegranate tree, don't you?'

Father raised her chin with a slender finger and brought his face close to hers. 'Persephone was forced to return to the underworld every year for every pomegranate seed she ate, leaving winter in her wake.'

'Remember, she was kidnapped by Hades?'

'Why don't we go inside and you can tell me the whole story?' Father asked. 'Amogh here will look after his little sister.'

His voice had turned husky. Amogh noticed his mother blushing. He watched his parents walk towards the house; Father looking back and calling out to Ketaki to be careful with the ruby and not wander too far. Amogh sighed; the morning was simply perfect. Father was back from his travels with a wonderful ruby and a wonderful story. A bird called out from the orange grove at the far end of the wall. A few pomegranate blossoms fell on his face, shaken by the warm breeze. Amogh felt sleepy. When he woke up, Ketaki and the ruby were gone.

They mounted a search and for many days and nights, Father, his friends and the servants searched for her everywhere – in the forests, the valleys and the streets and winding lanes of Rishikesh. Someone reported they had seen a little girl on a boat accompanied by a tall stranger wearing a black cowl; someone else said they saw her on a bus bound for Delhi. A third report put her on a horse cart going to Shivpuri. With every sighting, a new search was instituted. The family posted rewards and hired detectives, but Ketaki could not be found. One day, the police came and took Father away. He was accused of stealing the ruby. Their lands, orchards, cars and boats were confiscated and sold to recompense the owner. Only the house remained. By then, the servants were long gone, except for a few faithful retainers who had served with Amogh's grandfather. When Amogh would go to his mother's room to wake her up, he would find her on the balcony, leaning over the balustrade, gazing out at the horizon where the road lost itself in the mist that rode the Ganga. It obscured the riverbank and gave the shamble of temple towers and buildings a ghostly hue.

Mother began to age quickly; her hair lost its shine and her once luminous skin its glow. Amogh watered the pomegranate tree himself every day, but somehow it seemed to be shrinking; its twisted trunk looked smaller than it used to be. One day, he woke up to the sound of wailing and found his old ayah beating her head against the pomegranate tree. Mother swayed gently from one of its branches, her chin stooped on her chest, her hair floating loose in the wind, her toes dragging on the grass. Later, he learned that Father had died in prison the day before.

'From that day, the tree stopped flowering and bearing fruit. After a while, it died. But still, every day I water it,' said Amogh.

'Why?' Asananda was curious.

'Hope,' the fruit-seller replied. 'Hope that it will bloom again one day and happiness will return to my life. And so will Ketaki.'

A gentle mist descended over the garden, suffused with the pale pink of the sunset. The mist entered the ruined house, smoking through the destroyed windows and cavernous doorway, lingering in the corners. There was a flap of wings, a harsh cry, and a large raven flew overhead into the fog. A small sob escaped Asananda and flew away into the mist. The fruit-seller reached out and stroked the monk's face. 'You are crying,' he said in wonder. 'Who are you crying for?'

'You continue to water your tree, even though you are not sure your prayers would be heard,' the monk said. 'You have taught me how to hope and pray.'

'Hope is my strength,' the fruit-seller said.

The monk thanked him for the story and hoped that Ketaki would come back one day.

'I have to find something for the master,' he said. The fruit-seller nodded and disappeared into the cavernous shell of his house. The sun had spent the day and the spreading fog was drawing its mystery over the garden and the hillside. Asananda reminded himself to be careful while trudging through the bushes. Just then, his foot struck something small, hard and round. A brief gust of wind parted the strands of mist. Something red and glistening like a ruby lay at his feet, partially hidden in the grass. He stooped to pick it up. It was a pomegranate.

The monk uttered a joyful cry and ran back to the ruined house, shouting for Amogh to come and see what he had found. He went to each room only to find darkness. Amogh was nowhere to be seen.

When the monk stepped out of the building, the fog had lifted. He walked out of the garden, unmindful of the thorny bushes that tore at his sarong and the twigs that scratched at his arms and legs. He held the pomegranate tightly in his fist as if he was the bearer of a miracle. He quickened his steps, eager to meet Gyanananda and show him the pomegranate and tell him Amogh's tale.

The Monk Discovers Hope in a Box

Asananda found the master lounging on a wooden chair on the veranda of the ashram. He held the pomegranate out to him. Gyanananda received it with a gentle smile. He raised the fruit to his face and inhaled its fragrance deeply.

'You have brought me the fruit of the tree that does not bloom,' he said. 'You are a truly gifted disciple and my blessings are with you, now and forever.'

'It is Amogh who needs them the most,' Asananda protested.

'Amogh did not tell you the whole story,' the master said. 'When he came to meet me carrying a basket of fruit, I told him I would accept it only when he stopped watering the tree. He said he couldn't, since he hopes it will bloom one day, and that daily act of hope is what sustains his life. Then I told him the tree would yield fruit the day the tears of a compassionate man fell upon it.'

Asananda's eyes overflowed. He called out to Narayana – the omnipresent and the omniscient. He was filled with peace. The master took a bite of the fruit and sighed in contentment.

'Now go to the kitchen and ask the cook to serve you,' he said. 'You can stay here until it is time for me to send you to seek the

Book of Shiva. The Himalayas is where Shiva lives, dances and unravels the mysteries of life and death to those who seek and find him.'

'What is the Book of Shiva?'

'It is god's mystery. When you are ready, I will send you to find it,' the master said, munching on the pomegranate seeds, crackling between his strong, white teeth.

Gyanananda was a tiny man, barely five feet high. He was very fair and had a high forehead that reminded Asananda of a Mughal dome, as did the guru's small potbelly. It was partially covered by a saffron garment draped over the shoulders. He looked too young to be a guru presiding over an ashram of more than fifty monks and fifty-one young initiates. Some of the ascetics in the ashram, when they got together to smoke hashish in their clay chillums, would speculate on their guru's age. Some said he was around fifty, the son of a rich Brahmin who had married a second time and disinherited him. In his grief and abandonment, the young Gyanananda had left home to become an itinerant monk. His wanderings took him to many holy cities and sacred places of power. Other monks said he was over a hundred years old, having earned immortality through meditation in the Himalayas. Asananda knew this could be true. Time could, indeed, be slowed by learning from the ageless spirits who visited ascetics in caves high in the snowy mountains. Gyanananda looked around thirty-five.

For a year, Asananda lived in the ashram doing chores during the day and meditating in the morning and at night, but he couldn't unravel the mystery of his guru's age.

One day, he asked Gyanananda how old he was. The master laughed, his piercing eyes regarding his disciple with amusement.

'I do not know, Asananda,' he said. 'If you imagine the universe as a book, age is a paragraph. There are millions of paragraphs about everyone and everything and it takes many births for anyone to read their entire story.'

'Is it the Book of Shiva? Who wrote it? God?' the monk asked.

'Everyone in the Universe writes his own story, and god just chuckles when he reads some parts,' answered the guru.

'Where can I find my paragraphs?' the monk asked.

'Have faith, and you will. Faith is a path in the fog.'

'Where does it lead? To god?'

'Faith and hope,' the guru answered. 'The only place faith takes you to in the end is towards yourself. It is only then that you know whether the journey was worth it or whether you should retrace your steps. Journeys without hope take you nowhere.'

The monk pondered over this statement for a while.

'This reminds me of the story you told us during last week's sermon,' the monk said. 'Your version of Pandora's box.'

God gave Pandora a box but forbade her to open it. However, he knew that Pandora's curiosity would lead her to disobey him. As she lay awake at night with the forbidden box beside her, she kept hearing a little voice from inside the box, urging her to open the lid and set it free. One day, she couldn't bear it any longer. She opened it and evil came into the world; malevolent clouds seeded with the spirits of darkness, winged monsters of war, pestilence and death. In the end, flew out two tiny, luminous beings who fluttered in the air around Pandora's head, flapping their gossamer wings. As they fluttered exulting in their freedom, their luminosity became brighter and brighter until they resembled two flying stars.

'Thank you for opening the box,' they chorused.

'But what I did was terrible! I unleashed evil,' Pandora wailed.

'You released us as well. It was terrible, being trapped inside the box. Even evil needs us to exist. It was feeding off us and we gave it the strength to grow. When the world was first created, we were angels, glorious and powerful, but god shut us in too. He told us to wait, and that one day we would find our purpose. Inside the box, we were tortured by the monsters, though they couldn't devour us completely because we kept each other alive, dreaming that one day someone would liberate us.'

'Who are you?' Pandora asked.

'I am Hope,' the small being said. 'And I had lost all hope until you set me free.'

'I am Faith,' said the other. 'I survived because I had to keep my friend here alive.'

'What will happen to Faith if Hope itself loses hope?' asked Pandora in wonder.

'But I didn't, you see. Faith kept telling me to dream of the light and keep on dreaming. And now that I have found it, those who dream of light will find us too,' said Hope.

'I couldn't let him perish,' said Faith. 'I had to fight the biggest demon of them all, a cunning and persuasive creature called Doubt, which kept murmuring in our ears to give into the darkness because the world was born out of it and would end in it.'

'How did you know someone would come along and set you free?'

'We had each other,' they said. 'And now you have us.'

Gyanananda was teaching his disciples that hope lived both in darkness and in light and it needed faith to fly.

The monk remembered the first few days of the war; huddled in trenches and bunkers, waiting for the Pakistanis to attack. The soldiers in his platoon wrote long letters to their mothers, wives and lovers in the hope of returning home soon, even while they were certain of death. At night, he heard their screams as nightmares about death and pain attacked like the winged creatures of Pandora's box.

Asananda knew that men dared to dream, even when faith was difficult, because the hope that they would survive kept them going. One could not exist without the other.

After thinking about it all, Asananda told his guru a story about meeting a holy man who had finished dreaming, who started him on his journey to find the Book of Shiva.

The Monk and the Mountaineer
Who Smoked

Many years ago, the man who was to become the monk woke up after he died. He was in a room with white walls and a window that opened into a blue sky full of mountains wearing snow on their heads. As he lay wondering whether he was in heaven, a man and a woman in white coats came into the room.

'Are you angels?' he asked them.

They laughed.

'No, captain, we are doctors,' the man in the white coat said. 'You are in the Kargil Army Hospital.' He turned to the woman. 'It's the concussion. The mortar shell nearly blew his head off.'

'Why am I in hospital?' the captain asked.

'You were seriously injured in the shelling,' the woman said, patting his head gently. 'Don't you remember anything?'

The man shook his head. It made him mildly dizzy.

'I was dead. I remember dying in the ice,' he said. 'I remember meeting the Great Father in the snow.'

'Who?'

'He is the father of all men for eternity,' the captain replied. 'The Great Ape that lives in the mountains.'

The Great Father had gathered him up in powerful arms covered with silver-blue fur, on which little diamonds of frost glittered in the cold northern sun. He hugged him to his warm and furry chest; it was like being cradled in the bosom of the universe. He felt the pain ebb as the Great Father pulled sleep over him like a warm blanket and he dreamt he was being carried downhill swiftly in a blur of blue fur and white snow.

'You were dreaming, captain. You will be fine. Your wounds have healed. You will need counselling and some physiotherapy. Meanwhile, you should rest,' the male doctor said soothingly.

'Rest.' The woman doctor smiled at him. She had eyes as black as onyx.

'I've rested enough,' said the captain. 'Before I went to sleep, the Great Father said this war is over for me and another one lies ahead. I am to look for him in the snow, high up where the snow eagles live in the crevasses of the mountains.'

'When will this damned war end?' the captain heard the male doctor swear. 'The Pakistanis keep shelling us and we keep firing back. How many good men have I seen come here with pieces missing and how many have I seen leave in boxes. The politicians talk war and peace whenever it suits them.'

'Politicians make me sick,' the woman barked.

The captain watched the doctors' white-clad backs as they left the room. He tried to rise from his bed. He could. He flexed his hands and feet. Gingerly, he got off the bed and tested his balance. He felt mildly wobbly. Then the feeling eased.

He gazed at the mountains. The Great Father lived there. From his window, he saw a path that led up the slope, losing itself among the deodars that stood like sentries, guarding the foothills. The captain slowly walked out of his room, testing his steps slowly, until he found he could walk quite steadily. Discarded on olive-green benches on the veranda were piles of boots and overcoats belonging to wounded soldiers who had been brought in. Some coats were stained with blood. The captain chose a large overcoat with thermal insulation and pulled on a pair of boots that looked relatively new. It had bloodstains on the toes. He passed the hospital gates and the sentries; they did not stop him. Big Shaktiman army trucks painted in camouflage rattled in and out of the gates.

The captain walked on, leaving the hospital behind, reaching the mountain path he had seen from the window. He did not know where he was going or where he would sleep or whether he would simply freeze to death. He had faith in the dream he saw as he died. It would take him to the Great Father.

His grandmother had told him that the Great Father lived in the Himalayas, where all life began when two oceans collided. He blew life into the water. Some knew him as the Yeti or the Abominable Snowman. But Grandmother told him that he was the father of all men. He was Hanuman, the avatar of Shiva who lived in the primordial mountains, helping those who had lost their way while seeking the grace of Shiva.

The Himalayan peaks meditated in remote seclusion. The captain began to trudge along the climbing path. The stiffness in his limbs slowly wore off as he climbed higher.

Suddenly, he heard someone singing. He looked around, but there was only the endless whiteness that stretched as far as the eye could see. As he walked on, the song grew closer. He recognized it as a hymn to Shiva, one his grandmother would sing while she offered her prayers.

Shiva Shambho Shambho
Shiva Shambho Mahadeva
Hara Hara Hara Hara Mahadeva

Shiva Shambho Mahadeva
Hala Hala Dhara Shambho
Hey Anathha Nathha Shambho
Hari Om Hari Om Hari Om Namah Shivaya ...

The singer's voice was melodious. As he neared a curve on the rising path, the captain saw a holy man coming down. He was small of stature and carried a stout staff. A cloth bag was slung over his shoulder. He was naked except for a loincloth. The captain wondered why he didn't freeze to death. Seeing him, the ascetic smiled and raised a hand in greeting.

The wind blew a fragment of mist that enveloped them both for an instant and then dissipated. The captain could not recall where or when he had seen the ascetic, but he felt a sense of déjà vu.

'Aren't you freezing?' asked the captain.

The holy man shrugged and asked him if he had a smoke. The captain said he didn't smoke cigarettes.

The ascetic protested, 'Cigarettes are disgusting and serve no purpose, while hashish is Lord Shiva's substance. It is the smoke of other realms.'

If Lord Shiva smoked, why couldn't he? Shiva danced with his head and matted tresses wrapped in vapours of hashish, just like the clouds smoking on the mountaintops. Shiva's dance made the mountains tremble, the clouds flee in the sky and the holy river Ganga, which sprouted from his forehead, disgorge itself with such power that the plains flooded.

'Maybe I will smoke when Lord Shiva asks me to,' the captain said.

The holy man laughed. 'You speak as if you've read the Book of Shiva,' he said.

'What sort of book is it?' the captain asked.

'You will know when you read it,' the ascetic said, smiling widely.

His eyes twinkled merrily as he beamed. His teeth were very white against his dark skin, which was burnt by the sun at high altitudes. He pointed a thin, long finger back at where he had come from. 'Walk for three days and you will find a cave. Inside, you will find a leopard skin on the ground. Sit on it. You may, then, find Lord Shiva,' the holy man said.

'Is it necessary to sit in a cave to find Lord Shiva?' the captain asked curiously.

The ascetic laughed. 'It's not necessary to do anything to find Lord Shiva. If he wants to, he will find you himself. Meanwhile you wait, doing the ordinary things you do. It can be very boring, finding god.'

'How do you know all this? How do you know about the cave and the leopard skin?'

'Because I'm coming from there. I used to live there myself.'

'How long did you live there?'

'Maybe a hundred years. Or maybe for just a couple of years. I don't know. It doesn't matter.'

The soldier looked at the ascetic incredulously.

'You mean you are a hundred years old?'

'I don't remember.'

'Did you find god after reflecting for so long?' the captain asked, his voice spiced gently with derision. The holy man didn't seem to notice.

He said, 'I wasn't worthy. I was lucky. He found me.'

'Then what happened?'

The holy man looked puzzled.

'Then, nothing. I left the cave and now am on my way to Rishikesh to find an ashram to live in. Or to found one for others to live in. There I will teach those who have been waiting for me.'

The captain was confused. 'Why would they wait for you if they don't even know you?' he asked.

'Hope is not just about waiting for good things to happen. It's also about having the faith and the will to make them happen.'

'How can anyone teach others to make things happen?'

'By teaching nothing. It's the most difficult thing to teach and to comprehend. A great master is one who teaches nothing and the pupil understands everything.'

'You are talking rubbish. Can you teach me nothing?' the captain asked.

The holy man thought for a while. From the little bundle hung over his shoulder, he took out a small copper vessel. He stooped to fill it with ice. He asked the soldier to look into it. The captain peered in. The ice resembled a lump of coarse sugar. He touched it.

'Do you feel the cold?' the holy man asked. The captain nodded.

The ascetic began to blow on the ice. His breath made plumes in the crisp, high air. The captain began to perspire. The holy man's breath was warming the air. It became hot. Then hotter. He turned to look at the captain. Little pinpoints of fire burnt within his pupils. He thrust the copper vessel towards the captain.

'Look again,' he commanded. The captain looked.

'What is inside now?' the holy man asked.

'Water.'

'Earlier, there was ice. Now there is water that was once ice. What is in the water?'

'Nothing,' replied the captain. 'Just water.'

'Look again,' the ascetic said.

The captain looked. In the water, he saw reflected a familiar face. Far above it, clouds lounged sleepily in a deep blue sky. He blinked, and his own face stared back at him.

'I'm inside,' he said.

The ascetic laughed. He raised his hand and threw the water on the snow. It hissed with steam. He held out the vessel again for the soldier to look into.

'There is nothing now,' the captain said.

'Now do you understand? It's all in there. Both being and non-being.'

The captain bowed his head and thought for a while. 'Is that how one gets enlightened?' he asked the ascetic.

'No. You get enlightened by forgetting everything. And that's only part of it.'

'How do I find all the parts?'

The holy man threw the bundle over his shoulder, picked up the staff he had planted in the snow, gestured vaguely behind his shoulder and prepared to walk away.

'For that you have to become Shiva,' he said.

'Wait,' the captain called after him. 'How does one become Shiva? I thought there was only one Shiva.'

'Anyone can become Shiva, for he is the one who is eternally pure but also the one who purifies.'

'Life is transient. While there is good in man, he is also full of sin and evil. Then how can anyone become eternally pure?'

'Through suffering and the joy that it brings.'

'How does suffering bring joy?'

'When it ends.'

'Then one becomes pure?'

'Yes, for that is the purpose of the journey of man. Intense suffering forces you to be free of desire, which is what makes us human. It doesn't begin or end when you want, and hence reveals the futility of desire. When it ends at last, you are filled with a joy that expels everything else. Next, you become free of the joy because, at that moment, there is no longer anything to be sad about. You arrive at a stage where there are no opposites, only One.'

'Then what remains in a person?'

'Nothing.'

'If a person has nothing, how does he purify others?'

'By giving and taking without desiring anything for himself, just like the Ganga which receives them all, sinners and the good, children and the old, men and women. She accepts both corpses and lamps lit in her honour. She judges none and accepts all. All find salvation in her, because she represents the purity of Shiva. Starting from the Himalayas, she ends in the ocean, where life began. Thus, she begins from god and ends in god, just like our souls.'

The ascetic winked at the soldier, waved, and trotted down the slope. He passed behind a big boulder dressed in snow and disappeared into the whiteness below.

'Who are you?' the captain called after him.

'A mountaineer who lost his way years and years ago,' came the holy man's voice, slightly slurred in the wind.

Asananda finished his tale. His eyes met his master's. Gyanananda's eyes glowed with little pinpoints of fire. He laughed and patted his disciple on the back.

'So you remember how you found me,' the guru said. 'Now go and find yourself and become Shiva. Find the Book of Shiva.'

The Monk Meets Some Strange Ascetics

It was nearly noon when Asananda set out on his journey from Rishikesh to seek the Book of Shiva. When he started from the ashram after touching his master's feet, seeking his blessings, the day was already getting warm. He walked along the embankment and nodded to a group of ascetics who sat cross-legged in the shade of wind-frayed gazebos, smoking and chatting. Their tridents gleamed in the sun. Some of them wore only a single shabby loincloth, while others wore tattered, half-burnt shrouds of cadavers stolen from the cremation ground. Their bearded faces and bodies were smeared with ash, which gave their skin a corpse-blue tint. Their matted hair hung down to their shoulders in twisted uncombed coils or was wound in concentric circles ending in shaggy topknots above wrinkled brows and hollow cheeks. Thick garlands of holy rudraksha beads were looped around their necks, almost covering their lean chests. They looked at him with fierce eyes and then averted their faces angrily, as if he was an interloper who had interrupted some arcane conclave. The monk stopped and folded his palms, but they did not return his greeting.

'Learned masters,' he started, 'can you tell me where to find the Book of Shiva? I'm told I can find it in the Himalayas.'

One of the ascetics gave a loud rasping laugh.

'Do we look like sherpas or trekking guides?' he asked. 'Go away and leave us in peace.'

'I've heard of sadhus like you, who have conquered heat, cold, hunger and thirst by meditating in the Himalayas. I thought, perhaps, you could tell me where to find the book.'

They didn't answer. Asananda suspected they were aghoris – outcasts among holy men. They follow Bhairava – the fierce form of Lord Shiva. Shiva is said to have twenty-five forms. Aghoris meditate on their savage deity at night, sitting on the bones of the dead in cremation grounds. They seek Kali, Shiva's black-skinned consort who came into being before eternity and represents death and the end of time. Kali is the goddess of time and her lord, Shiva, is kaal – time itself. She wears a garland of skulls and a skirt made of dismembered heads and arms. She is the mistress of demons and the queen of the hordes. Aghoris are a monistic Hindu order, who believe that everything comes from, and is united with, the same substance.

For the aghori, Shiva is the final reality. When the aghori eats human flesh from the partially burnt corpses floating in the Ganga after cremation, he believes he is consuming Shiva's flesh. When he meditates sitting on a cadaver, he becomes one with death; and hence one with Shiva. He embraces taboos in order to transcend them; and the more bizarre they get, the more powerful he becomes. The three prongs of Shiva's trident symbolize Will, Knowledge and Action. Its column denotes the spinal cord, along which travels the sushumna nadi – the most important energy channel in the body. The kundalini is the occult serpent that rises through the nadi as the aghori perfects his outlandish worship, through which, in the end, he achieves ultimate freedom. Thus, he acknowledges no institution; he is nobody's servant and nobody's master. He is Shiva.

Asananda knew that all paths lead to the same destination, just as all the roots of a tree seek the same water source. He also knew that he would not slake his thirst from the dark stream the aghoris drank from; his was not their way of seeking knowledge in charnel houses, necrophiliacs who ate the flesh of corpses and covered their naked bodies with the ashes of the dead. He simply walked along a path that seemed charted for him and he suspected his mysterious master had some role in deciding it. Asananda realized that some journeys were undertaken along paths that had never existed before; they simply unfolded on their own with each step taken by the traveller, like a new stream finding its way. He smiled and walked on.

'Hey, sadhu who is asking for the Book of Shiva,' an aghori shouted after him in a hoarse voice, 'look for the one who rows the boat!'

Asananda turned around. But the ascetics had gone back to smoking and chatting among themselves.

Near the embankment steps, a solitary pilgrim was taking a ritual dip in the river, his nose gripped between his thumb and the forefinger of his right hand in the traditional Hindu gesture of ablution. The other hand was placed on his head as if he was saluting the climbing sun. An ashram's gong pounded in the distance, agitating the crows that fluttered up from treetops, cawing harshly. From the dark veranda of a ruined building, a blind beggar aggressively demanded alms. A white Brahma bull tethered to a young peepal tree shook its head repeatedly to disperse persistent flies; the bells around its neck rippled and tinkled, and their sound brought a distant memory to the monk's mind. He thrust it aside.

Rishikesh summoned all sorts of people who came bearing burdens big and small; of secrets pregnant with sorrow, hate, guilt, violence or helplessness. It is believed that bathing in its waters cleansed one of all sin and took the devotee closer to moksha – the final liberation of the soul.

It is from Rishikesh that the river Ganga – bearing the sins of pilgrims bathing in its myriad ghats – left the Himalayan foothills and moved on to the plains.

The monk remembered sitting with his master one day on the riverbank near the ashram.

'O Asananda, it is a river of unbearable pain. It is also the river of hope. The hopes of generations of sinners swim in its tides. When I bathe in it, I feel them like ghostly fishes tearing at my skin,' Gyanananda said, softly grieving. 'I wonder, where this river, in which mankind unburdens itself, unburdens itself?' Asananda asked.

Gyanananda thought about his disciple's question, sitting by the quiet river.

'Let me tell you a story about unburdening,' he said after a while.

The Monk Hears of the Boatman's Secret

'Once upon a time, there was a boatman who rowed souls across the Vaitarna – the River of Death,' spoke Gyanananda. These unfortunates were fearful of what lay ahead once they reached Yamalok – the land ruled by the God of Death. On the Vaitarna's shore across stood a great lighthouse that cast its beacon into the endless night, showing the boatman the way to bring the souls home and take back those whose time had come to be reborn. He was tired of rowing, because he had been at it for what seemed centuries. He was obsessed by the desire to be free of his grim, cold task and wanted to get off his boat, even if it was on the shore of death, so that he could tarry awhile near the lighthouse and feel the warmth of its light soothe the ache in his chilled bones. Each time the boat landed at the Pier of Souls, the boatman would ask the passengers if anyone wanted to take his place, and that it would buy them time before meeting Death. Some of them hesitated and then refused, while others decisively got off the boat and just walked towards whatever waited for them. The boatman would sadly shake his head and row back to collect the next load of his doomed cargo. He had a secret. Once upon a time, he, too, was a soul who had accepted the offer of the previous boatman so that he could live and was doomed to row forever – or until the next soul fell for the trick.

'Why did the souls refuse, Asananda? After all, they would get the gift of life again.'

The monk said he did not know. He thought the boatman was offering a damn good deal, pun unintended.

'It was fear and hope that forced the souls to refuse,' the master said. 'Fear of monotony; of rowing endlessly until the next fool came along. And the hope that something good waited for them in the land of death, even if they had been bad in this life.'

'Did the boatman ever find his replacement?'

One night, the boatman found a stranger waiting at the foot of the lighthouse. Seeing the boat draw up to the pier, he approached it.

'Who are you and where do you want to go?' asked the boatman.

'I am the light keeper and I want to go across to the other shore, where I can find a physician to cure me,' the stranger answered. 'After so many years of being the light keeper, my eyes are beginning to fail me. I can no longer bear the heat and brightness of the lamp. Can I borrow your boat while you take my place for a while? I wish to see my family.'

The boatman was delighted at his unexpected good luck. At last, he would be able to live in brightness and warmth, while the previous occupant would have to row the boat of souls forever in the cold, immortal night. He wasn't going to tell the light keeper that he would never be free of his duty until a new boatman was found. What he did not know was that the lighthouse keeper had been waiting for ages for someone to take his place so that he could stop caring for the great lamp that had affected his eyes and scorched his skin. Alone in his high cabin, he had nobody to talk with, and felt lonely and dispirited, aching to be with the living once more. He had his eyes on the boat for a long time and had longed to become its boatman. He had thought how wonderful it would be to feel the freedom of gliding upon the tides of the Vaitarna and enjoy the company of souls and feel that he belonged to the great throng of humanity – dead or alive. He planned to climb ashore once he reached the opposite bank and go home where his wife and children waited for him. He had lost track of time waiting to take over the boat. He also didn't know that now that he has relieved the boatman, he would be doomed to row the boat of the dead till another took over.

After handing over the oars to the eager lighthouse keeper, the boatman climbed up the steps of the lighthouse where the huge lamp shone like a sun. It dazzled him. He was not worried about going blind, for he could always pull his cowl down to cover his eyes if the light became too bright. As he watched the new boatman gingerly pull away from the pier, he suddenly remembered something. He called after the former light keeper, 'Do I light the lamp when I wake up? And when do I put it out before going to sleep?'

'You can never sleep,' the new boatman's voice echoed over the river of death. 'Because you cannot put off the lamp, because it is the Beacon of Hope.'

The monk thought long about the story, but did not get its point.

'The lesson of the story is that hope can trick you as well as save you,' Gyanananda said. 'When you are possessed by a desire so much that you become blind to everything else, you will never see the trap hope lays out to test you.'

Standing by the embankment, Asananda turned to look back at the ashram where his guru had given him the little wisdom he possessed as well as sanctuary. He was grateful that Gyanananda had sent him on a quest: everyone needs a quest. Or else, life doesn't have direction and one gets lost.

Asananda walked towards Lakshman jhoola – the narrow iron bridge that connected the populous part of Rishikesh to the quieter side of town. It led to a shrine by a holy pool where the god Ram and his brother Lakshman are believed to have bathed after killing the great, wise demon Ravana, and were cleansed of the venialities of war.

'Will I be able to shed my sins on this journey?' the monk asked the Ganga. 'Will I be able to avoid my journey trapping me with the temptation of freedom without knowledge?'

The river didn't answer.

The Monk Meets the Rower of Fate

The Himalayan wind swam down across the distances, gliding along the tops of pine and peepal, skimming the silver brocade of the waves of the Ganga while rushing down ancient rocks glistening in darkness and light. It carried the primordial smells of the forest; the heady fragrance of wild flowers that grew on meadows shawled with grass, and the fresh scent of living water. As he crossed the bridge, the monk Asananda glanced towards the pier below at the end of a long flight of timeworn stone steps that tumbled down in unruly descent towards the river. Small groups of passengers stood around chatting, smoking or simply staring across the water, waiting for the ferry. A woman in a colourful sari pulled away a small boy who was squatting at the edge of the wooden platform, peering down into the water. A river bird swooped down and flashed up again in a single graceful moment, holding a fluttering silvery fish in its beak. Small wooden boats, darkened with age and tied to decaying log poles in the shallows of the riverbed, rocked lazily in the gentle slaps of the tide. The monk could see the ferry crawling beneath the bridge and the flash of a camera wink brightly in the afternoon.

He hoisted his satchel over his shoulder, took up his staff and walked down the steps. The urchins hired by boatmen to finagle passengers left the monk alone, for they knew that sadhus did not have much money; some even cursed boatmen who dared to ask them for the fare. In Rishikesh, the city of sin and absolution, everyone was afraid of curses.

At the far end of the pier, Asananda saw a solitary boat tied to a pole. No urchin tried to commandeer passengers for its boatman, who sat at the prow, wearing a dark shawl draped like a hood over the head, although the afternoon was warm. He could not see the face, but noticed that the boatman's arms, which held the oars with the casual ease of an experienced rower, were dark and sinewy. The boatman's form radiated a proud solitude that compelled the monk to walk towards the boat.

'Will you take me?' he asked.

The boatman nodded and the monk threw his satchel into the boat and stepped on to the wooden planks nailed across the sides for passengers to sit upon. The boatman leaned back and pulled at the oars, and the little craft moved away from the pier, slipping into the flow with practiced ease. The hood slipped away from the boatman's face. It was a woman.

She had a dark, oval face imprinted with fine wrinkles and a sorrowful mouth. She would have been beautiful, if it was not for the livid scar that furrowed her face diagonally across her nose from her left temple to the corner of her upper lip.

'I was told to look for you,' Asananda said as the boat glided across the khakhi-coloured water.

The woman laughed. 'It must be the aghoris, they are always asking me to have sex with them.'

She saw the monk's face and laughed again. The scar rippled, as if a serpent hid inside her face. 'Are you thinking how anyone would want to have sex with someone like me, whose face looks like that of a demoness?'

The monk shook his head. 'Appearances do not interest me,' he said. 'But be careful of the aghoris. They can be cruel.'

'Aghoris are cruel only when the demons of the charnel grounds possess them. Otherwise, like all sadhus, they seek to be one with god. Only, they believe in the dark Vedas to awaken the kundalini that lies coiled within us all. But my kundalini is this river, and one day I shall find salvation by it.'

'You are a strange boatman, or should I call you boat lady, who talks to strange monks about kundalini and moksha.'

'This is Rishikesh. Here, everyone is after moksha. All who come here believe that salvation can be bought by giving money to gurus and performing expensive pujas for the gods in the hundreds of temples and ashrams around. If salvation can be bought, then why does one need to try so hard to reach god?' the boat lady said.

The monk bowed his head in thought.

'Guilt drives most people to seek salvation,' she said. 'They do not seek god out of love, only out of fear.'

As she rowed, pulling backward and forward, sweat glistened on her face. She closed her eyes each time she sculled. Her hands gripped the oars firmly, belying a strength that wasn't apparent. Suddenly, she let the boat drift and opened her eyes that were too large for her oval face.

'You didn't tell me where to go, monk,' she said.

'Across.'

'There is no "across the river",' she said. 'Anywhere you stand is across the river. It depends on where you want to go.'

'I have to go as far as my guru wants me to,' he replied. 'You can take me to the other shore. I'll walk from there.'

'Didn't the aghoris tell you to look for me? Now that you have found me, don't you want to discover what it is that you have found?'

'All I want to find is the Book of Shiva,' said the monk. 'Just set me down on the bank across and I will be on my way,' the monk protested.

'All discoveries take time and come at a price,' the boatwoman said.

Her eyes sought his out, forcing them to meet her compelling gaze. He saw dark whirlpools and the gleam of the moon on water.

'I do not want money,' she said as she rowed on. 'You can pay me with something else.'

The monk raised his eyebrows. The woman laughed.

'Don't be afraid, I'm not suggesting anything scandalous. Let me tell you a story.'

The Monk and the Lullaby Maker

The wind that skimmed the surface of the river was loaded with distant sounds and scents, as if it had collected lost fables and fretful passions during its long journey.

'I was a rich merchant's daughter and I grew up in a beautiful haveli near Rishikesh,' she began. Her name was Roopvati and she lived in a three-storeyed house with many rooms and scores of servants. The house was on the riverbank and the Ganga was always visible through the arches of its gilded windows. Roopvati had her own suite and many maids and a ghat – a private bathing enclave – in the river, which was accessed by a flight of long stone steps. The walls of her suite were painted with murals that depicted the blue god Krishna frolicking with maidens in the Brindavan forest and playing his flute as his lover, Radha, listened with her eyes closed, smiling. Peacocks danced on green grass; colourful parrots flew across blue skies with small white clouds sketched on them; the orange trees were in eternal bloom, each fruit like a small, orange sun. From her jharokha – a traditional balcony that juts out of the wall, supported by corbels and embellished with trellises on the sides – Roopvati could watch the sun set over the Ganga in a slow arc, turning the rippling water into a purple-hued garment.

Far away, the lights would come on one by one as Rishikesh was reincarnated in the dusk as an illuminated, magical maze. Roopvati's favourite maid would comb her long, black hair and deepen her large eyes with charcoal. Her toenails and fingernails would be painted red, and the maid would draw elaborate paisley patterns with henna on the soft skin of her arms and legs. She would massage her mistress's face with rose water and rub scented oil on her neck and shoulders. Sometimes, the caresses would make her fall asleep and the maid would cover her with a shatoosh shawl and tiptoe away. She would sleep to the low purl of the Ganga and the cries of night birds would brush against the edges of her dreams.

One night, when the stars were bright and clouds lay languorously across the moon, Roopvati woke up to the sound of singing. She rose from her bed and looked out into the night and saw a boatman rowing in the distance. He was singing as he rowed with slow, sure strokes. His boat was silver in colour. Its reflection rippled in the black water like a mirror being disturbed. In the great vault of the night, his song glided and dipped like a dark swan.

Enchanted, Roopvati did not notice that she had taken up her tanpura and had begun to pluck its strings. The boatman paused as he heard the sudden melody of the instrument and looked towards the façade of the sleeping house where only one doorway blazed with light. He rowed on, his song growing louder and sweeter as Roopvati's instrument escorted his voice; slowly fading as the silver boat passed beyond the curtain of night.

Every night, Roopvati waited for the boatman. Every night, his song arrived before his boat from behind the bend in the Ganga, and she would be ready with her tanpura. But he never came close enough for her to catch a glimpse of his face, even though often she would lean far out over the balcony, almost falling into the water. Sometimes, he would raise a hand in a lazy salute, and she would wave back frenetically. Often, the moon would tantalizingly outline his form or an angle of his face, and she would yearn to see him close up and hold him. Roopvati imagined him as tall, strong and muscular with bright eyes and a soft smile. In her mind, she ran her hands over his smooth, golden skin and traced the outlines of his warm sensual mouth; she felt the thickness of his black hair slide through her fingers. Each time his boat faded into the darkness, she felt a tiny part of her depart, and float away in the Ganga like a raven's feather, tossing in the spindrift of the silver boat. As dusks passed, she felt her yearning grow into a great abyss, whose walls were mossy with despair.

Soon people in the house began to notice that she was growing pale and thin, as if some illness was consuming her. They consulted doctors, hakeems and ayurvedic physicians, but none could diagnose what was wrong. They gave her pills to swallow and syrups to drink; they poured medicinal oils on her head and massaged her temples with unguents, but Roopvati descended deeper into the twilight within her, where the river flowed as a deep and low melody on which she sailed towards a receding shore. She ate and drank little, and lay on her bed in a stupor all day, until the evening temple bells announced the advent of nightfall. Then she became restless to go to her balcony. In a few weeks, she had become so weak that the servants had to carry her at her behest and place her on the divan on the jharokha.

Only when she heard the boatman's song chasing the fleeing dusk would she sit up with sudden energy and reach for her tanpura. She would play on, even after the silver boat had disappeared, and her slender fingers would start to bleed. Her favourite maid was the only one who knew what was wrong with Roopvati.

One day, worried about her mistress, she told Roopvati's mother about the boatman. She, in turn, told her husband, who became furious at the thought of his beautiful daughter, who was the heiress to his immense fortune and could marry any young, handsome and rich man, being in love with a strange boatman. He ordered his servants to find him.

The next two nights passed as Roopvati waited for her boatman and his song, her sighs softening the night. But the silver boat did not appear. When she could not see it the next day either, she became very agitated. Her mother was worried that her daughter would waste away and die. 'Don't worry,' the merchant told his wife. 'It's a matter of time before she recovers. Then we'll let her choose a husband from among all the virile young men of the city, and she will forget her boatman.'

That evening, Roopvati was awakened by the sound of something grating against the stone steps of her ghat. A heron cried harshly from across the water. The girl rose and looked down and saw the silver boat beached upon the thin sliver of white sand beside the steps. Inside lay a crumpled form. She gave a small cry and rushed down. She climbed on the boat and took the dead boatman in her arms. She turned his face towards her and, with a shock, realized that he was not what she had imagined him to be. His dark skin was already turning dirty purple with the humours of death. His legs were too short for his torso, and his closed eyes were small and slanted. Only the arms were long and muscular; they bore deep wounds from swords and knives, which he had received while resisting his attackers. His throat had been cut. As a final, mutilation, his attackers had slashed his face diagonally from forehead to the mouth. But somehow, the bizarre mischief of murder had disarranged his violated features in such a way that he looked heartbreakingly handsome – a face that could've haunted her dreams. Roopvati fainted.

When she came to, it was dawn. The river was turning silver, and the sleepy mountains were emerging from the departing darkness. She took up the oars of the silver boat and pulled away from the ghat. She did not know where she was bound. She knew the river hid treachery in its tides, but it could also be gentle and protective; a mother of water. As the boat moved upstream, she felt her hands grow stronger, rowing against the current. The water was swelling and heaving, and Roopvati tried to keep the silver bier afloat. The first drops of rain stung her face as the sky darkened and opened, and the little boat was suddenly caught in a swell and capsized. Roopvati saw the body fall away into the river, which received it in a maternal embrace. She clung to the upturned boat as the river buffeted her. She did not care whether she lived or died; as darkness descended on her, riding the rain, a primeval instinct made her cling to the keel of the boat. When she came to, she found that the silver boat had righted itself and she was lying curled up inside. The Ganga had decided to be merciful.

'The Ganga brought me back to Rishikesh. Ever since, I have been rowing along this river,' said the boat lady. 'Most of the silver paint has peeled off over the years, and the boat has black, mouldy patches on its sides. But it's sturdy and doesn't leak.'

'How did you get the scar?' the monk asked.

'It was a gift,' the woman replied. 'After the storm, when I woke up in the boat, I felt my face was burning. I touched my face and felt the throbbing of the scar. It felt alive.'

'How did that happen?'

Roopvati gave a harsh laugh. 'Everyone bears the scar of a great love,' she said. 'In my case, it chose to manifest itself on my face.'

'Where do you live?' the monk asked.

'I don't live anywhere,' she replied. 'I go where the tides take me. At night, I tie the boat beside the ghats, and sometimes I sleep in it. The sun has blackened my skin and bleached my hair, and my face frightens some people. But my body is still desirable, and so I do not go hungry.'

'Don't you get passengers?' the monk asked.

'Sometimes. Mostly men. The women are scared to get on my boat, once they see my face. Perhaps, they feel I am cursed; maybe they fear my scar will bite them. But it doesn't bother me. I simply ask them to pay me in the only currency I take.'

'What is your payment?' asked Asananda.

'Songs,' Roopvati said. 'I earn songs.'

The monk understood.

'Have you found his?'

She shook her head sorrowfully. 'Only a few snatches here and there. Sometimes, parts of a tune. But never the whole song.'

Roopvati rested the oars and, for a while, they drifted along peacefully. A pair of white storks flew overhead. A fish leaped, like a sudden hope, and disappeared back into the water.

'You can never find what is not yours,' the monk said at last. 'It was his song, and it can never be yours. He sang it not for you, but to himself, or a lover, as he rowed from wherever he came to wherever he was going. You happened to hear it one day, and imagined it was being sung for you. And that it was your song.'

'Perhaps you are right, monk,' the boatwoman said bitterly. 'But that doesn't stop me from searching. If I find the whole song, perhaps, I will find myself. That is the way of love.'

Asananda bowed his head. 'Every journey has its own song that a traveller hums as he walks along,' he said.

'What is yours?' the boatwoman asked.

'I don't know. But the only song I remember is the one I heard when I was a small child, and that too in bits and pieces,' he replied. 'It was a lullaby. My mother sang it to me when I was very young.'

'Sing it to me, then, monk,' said Roopvati.

'It's in Malayalam, you wouldn't understand.'

'Lullabies in any language can be understood,' said the boatwoman. 'Please, sing yours.'

The monk cleared his throat and sang tunelessly.

Omana thingal kidavo,
Nalla komala thamara poovo,
Poovil niranja madhuvo
Pari poornendhu thante nilavo
Puthan pavizha kodiyo
Cheru thathakal kochum mozhiyo...

'It's an old lullaby,' the monk explained. 'When I would be stubborn and refuse to sleep, my mother would carry me on her hip and take me outside to show me the moon. And she would sing in a low voice, asking the moon who I was. Was I its darling? Or a honey-filled flower? Was I a new-born coral reef, was I the prattle of parrots or the sweet song of a nightingale ... There is more of it along these lines, and she would keep on singing until I drifted off to sleep.'

'You are on your way towards some place looking for something that is important to you. But do you remember where you come from, your home, monk?' asked Roopvati. 'Is there anyone waiting for you?'

'Narayana Narayana,' the monk murmured, closed his eyes and let himself be swept by the purl of the river to another time and place.

The Monk and the Detritus
of Old Journeys

Sitting in the moving boat, Asananda felt something tugging at his mood, changing it as if a tide had begun to flow within him, bearing fragmented memories like fallen leaves.

A return. An attic. A dusty iron box full of baby clothes wrapped in fragile paper. Old postcards and yellowed letters. A large tin trunk that held a neatly pressed and folded air force uniform and an Indian flag. Locks of hair in a small, velvet-lined box with mother of pearl inlay. Grandmother's footfalls echoing in the rooms. A broken dust-covered bangle that lay beside a ruined window. Shards of cooking pots scattered on a kitchen floor, guarded futilely by sooty walls. Years of neglect had almost erased a home.

In his army captain's crisp uniform, he felt like an outsider in a once-familiar place. A tree's shadow fell on the yellowing courtyard wall to make an ogre's hand, which had swayed menacingly through childhood nights. He looked for scribbles in secret places, where only those who were looking for them could find them. On the floor of a small, familiar room, a young girl's faded photograph had fallen sometime ago from between the leaves of a school book, which now lay with its pages in disarray. Her twin braids were intertwined with red ribbons that formed hibiscus-like bows on either side of a smiling face, her eyes dark with kohl and squinting against the sun; for a passing moment, the scent of jasmine flirted with the wind and a peal of distant laughter danced out from memory.

The captain wandered through the naked rooms. Empty squares of absent pictures greeted him from the discoloured walls pocked with nail marks. Huge gaps in the roof yawned, through which he could see the weather-mottled rafters stretched like Jurassic bones, challenging the sky. Among the litter on the cracked floor lay an Ace of Clubs. He smiled, as if he had just heard a joke told so many times before, it was little more than a pleasant memory from when he would sit on the veranda of the house, playing cards with classmates who no longer wrote him letters.

He was ready to close the chapter. He only had to sign some papers, and then he would be free of it all. Free of the house, its memories and the nostalgia that always haunted him. He would fly back to Delhi, to his apartment in the Cantonment. With the money from the sale of the house, he could buy the cottage in the Himalayan foothills, which he had always dreamt of owning. He touched the dark wood of the ancient wooden pillars that supported the slope of the tiled roof in covenant, interlinking his fingers with the phantom touches of his ancestors on the varnish. He watched the sunset spread its arms in the sky like a dervish dancing with god. He thought he heard his mother calling him from inside the house and smelt the peculiar sharp aroma of the Nilgiris coffee she used to make. He turned around, almost answering her, but there was no one inside the dying house.

The garden was overgrown, the courtyard upswept and pitted with rubble. In the middle of all the decay stood a small quadrangular stone structure with a holy basil plant growing on top, as if the devouring years hadn't happened at all; a square platform of whitewashed brick, with little naves to shelter the sacred flames. He remembered Mother and Grandmother placing lit clay lamps in the naves at dusk, chanting the name of Narayana to keep the darkness and its creatures at bay. The captain noticed that the basil plant still flourished after so many years, the aroma of its green leaves tempering the evening. He picked a leaf and rubbed between his fingers. Its aromatic touch soothed him strangely. To his surprise, he found it was damp; a bit sticky. He bent down to peer at the nave, and found a little earthen lamp, its sides stained with oil. Someone had lit it recently, and he smelt jasmine in the air. He looked across the overgrown garden through the old trees towards the neighbouring house that sulked behind the mossy wall. For a moment, he fancied he saw a dark shape that quickly disappeared into the shadows behind a wooden pillar; caught a glimpse of red ribbons. He glimpsed the swing suspended from the branch of the giant mango tree that stood proudly in the midst of the chaotic garden, swaying lazily in the wind. He smiled at old memories and walked over, expecting to see a ruined wooden plank rotting away from the rusting iron chains.

The phone in his pocket buzzed. It was the realtor calling, impatient to know when he could sign off on the sale. He didn't answer. He would simply let it be. Standing by the swing, he was surprised to see that its wooden seat looked polished to a shine, as if someone had been using it every day. He frowned and looked towards the neighbouring house, where he fancied he saw two pigtails bound with red ribbons, but there was only the play of twilight and shadows. He sighed and sat on the swing, and was lifted backwards when his shoe kicked the ground gently in reflex. He closed his eyes, leaning back into space, and waited as his mind slowly filled with the past.

The rocking of the boat shook Asananda from his reverie. Feeling Roopvati's hand on his shoulder, he opened his eyes. 'Tell me about your home, monk. Tell me about your love,' she said.

'It was all so long ago that I don't remember,' Asananda said. 'All I am is what I am now. A monk in search of the Book of Shiva.'

'Then please sing your mother's lullaby to me once again, it is the only thing you remember from before you became a monk,' the boatwoman said. 'I want to feel the love once more, the love of a mother, like the Ganga has for all of us, her children.'

The monk nodded, closed his eyes and sang. His voice took on a new timbre, as if the soul of a long dead boatman who rowed a silver boat had joined in. Tears filled the eyes of both the woman and the monk, each one crying for a different reason – one for a memory that had set her free at last and the other in gratitude for a love that he was able to remember, long after he had walked away from all that it represented.

'Now I know why the aghoris asked you to look for me, because you had a message for me,' Roopvati said, wiping away her tears. 'Each person meets someone with a message meant only for that one. It shows the final path. You have to keep looking and waiting for the bearer of your message.'

'What is the message you think I have brought you?' the monk asked.

'It is such a simple one, and all the while I've been searching for complex meanings to my misfortune,' she said, sadly. 'You brought me the message of the lullaby. It is the first song a child hears, which makes it smile, and the first song that puts it to sleep, safely. Lullabies drive away nightmares, allowing the child to dream. As we grow old, we forget our lullabies and our first dreams, leaving us with little to soothe our many fears. And we go into the night without the comfort of love.'

'I never thought of it that way,' said the monk. 'You are wise.'

'No, just happy that I met you,' she said. 'Now that I have found my meaning, I realize one more thing. There is no need to fear the future. On the other shore, Death waits to sing us our final lullaby. If you realize that, you will know peace. There is no need to struggle.'

'Om namo Narayana,' the monk praised the name of god.

'I'm tired, will you row for a while?' the boatwoman asked.

Roopvati leaned forward and passed the oars. The monk took them and she gave him a smile so brilliant that it seemed as if the moon had broken out of the clouds. As if by some unexpected enchantment, the lines on her face softened and vanished for a moment. Her lips became ruby red and her hair gleamed black and thick, and the monk glimpsed her as she once was: waiting on her trellised, pink balcony for her lover's song. Then her face returned to its scarred, wrinkled form as she leaned backwards and entered the river, her arms reaching out to the sky, as if in ecstasy. The Ganga cast its immortal mantle over her, taking her where the lullaby of its undertides would rock her to sleep.

'Narayana! Narayana!' Asananda cried out, invoking the Supreme One who rests on primordial water, 'narah', created by 'Nara', the One who Came First and lives in his abode, the 'ayana,' and therefore is the resting place of all.

A Strange Wanderer, Riding a Bull and Witnessing a Miracle

As the monk rowed on, Mother's lullaby refused to leave him, bringing discarded memories of childhood back. He remembered playing noughts and crosses on the veranda of his grandmother's house. The floor, laid more than a century ago, was cool and paved with large, red rectangular tiles. The ancient architects of Kerala had used a traditional mixture of red oxide powder, ground limestone, clay and eggs to make the tiles. The boy drew lines with chalk on the red surface. On each square he placed a manjadikuru – the seed of the kunda mani tree, which his grandmother explained was a lucky wish tree. The bright red manjadikurus were slightly elliptical in shape, smooth with a black spot at the tip, which gave them the look of a bright red eye. His grandmother said manjadikurus were the eyes of the small gods.

'What are the small gods, Grandmother?'

'They are everywhere. Every person is born with a small god looking after him or her.'

'Where is mine?'

'You'll know someday.' Grandmother smiled mysteriously and ruffled his hair.

The boy imagined the small gods watching as he played his game. Perhaps one of them was his. He would change sides with himself when he had to play the other person, whom he called his small god.

A sudden tinkling of bells disturbed his concentration. He looked up from his game, towards the courtyard. There they stood, the sadhu in saffron and his white karma bull. One moment the great courtyard had been empty, the shade of the mango trees swaying lazily on the paved earth; hens clucking and scampering across the yard on which the shadow of the roofed gateway lengthened imperceptibly. Then suddenly the sadhu and his bull were there; he holding a giant brass trident in one hand and a red rope tied around the bull's neck in the other. The animal was large, white, and had a huge hump. Its muzzle was black, wet and velvety. Its horns were decorated with cowrie shells and tiny copper bells. More bells were sewn into braided red ropes tied loosely around its neck. They also bordered a piece of red cloth, shiny with cheap golden embroidery, which was draped over the beast's body. The bull bellowed low and deep as it tossed its head, and the tinkling of bells made the boy think that the afternoon was dancing. He was surprised that Chandu – part Alsatian and part mongrel – tied to a wooden stake, usually used to tether frisky calves, did not bark. He just lay there, looking up at the visitors with mournful eyes in his long tawny face that rested on his front paws.

'Is anyone home?' the sadhu asked the boy. 'My bull is hungry. So am I.'

His saffron sarong came down to below his knees. His legs were tanned and muscled. His broad chest, matted with white hair, was covered with rosaries of rudraksha beads. His forehead was painted across with a great streak of vermillion. He beamed, white teeth like lightning in a sunburnt face.

'Come here,' he called out. 'Do you like my bull?'

The boy left his game and went up to them. He caressed the bull's flanks. Its skin felt like velvet.

'Do you want to ride my bull?' asked the sadhu.

'Oh yes, may I?' the boy said, his eyes growing wide, his voice rising with excitement.

The holy man nodded, lifted him up and placed him on the bull's back. The boy felt he was sitting on a great snowy mountain. The bull's hump was like a small hillock.

'How do you feel?' asked the sadhu.

'Like a small god,' answered the boy. The ascetic's eyes twinkled.

'Did you know that there actually is a small god? Others seek the big god without having found the small god first. Always listen to the small god and he will show you the way.'

'Unni, what are you doing? Come down immediately,' his grandmother's voice whipped across the air. From his tall perch, the boy looked towards the veranda. He saw Grandmother emerging like a spirit in white from the cool darkness of the house. She was staring at the sadhu. She paused on the threshold for an instant, framed in the doorway, which was carved out of old mahogany. She was frowning. She stepped out on to the veranda and came swiftly down the steps. The diamond pin on her aquiline nose sparkled. In her starched white, long-sleeved blouse and sarong, her dark hair streaked with white on the sides and tied in a knot at the nape, her slender shoulders pulled back, Grandmother seemed like a stern goddess. The sadhu didn't seem perturbed.

'Narayana, Narayana!' he greeted her. 'He is safe to sit on; he is a karma bull. You know the bull is Lord Shiva's mount. And now, your little boy is a little Shiva.'

Grandmother stared at the sadhu's face. Her expression had changed into shock. Then her face closed into itself.

'Some gruel for me and some hay for my bull, and we'll be on our way,' the sadhu said, nodding towards the giant mounds of golden hay stacked at the far end of the yard near the cattle sheds.

'Put my grandson down,' she said quietly. 'I'll tell the servants to get you some food. And some hay for your animal.'

The sadhu lifted the boy and placed him gently on the ground. Grandmother held her arms out and he ran into them.

'Were you afraid?' she asked. 'Don't worry, I've got you now.'

The boy shook his head in the folds of her skirt. He didn't tell her he wasn't afraid of sadhus. They fascinated him.

Often they came to his house to beg for food or money. They stood in the courtyard, sunspots falling on their faces and among the dusty folds of their saffron attire. With unruly beards – some knotted at the tip – matted tresses framing sunburnt faces and wearing frayed robes, they looked like strange, miraculous beings who were harbingers of outlandish miracles. Some were young with black beards and muscled limbs.

Grandmother shooed them away. Those who came with drugged snakes curled around their necks, partly meant to frighten the householder and partly to prove their magic powers, were threatened by Chandu, whose frenzied barking and frothing jaws were enough to make any unwelcome visitor beat a hasty retreat.

Chandu rarely barked at the old monks. The boy felt they were nameless prophets who could perform the most wonderful magic that silenced the dog. They came asking for alms, food, water and old clothes.

'Be wary of the young swamis,' Grandmother warned the boy. 'They are thieves and murderers who have run away from home after committing some terrible crime.'

'How do you know, Grandmother?'

'Why else would anyone run away from home? They must have done something heinous and fled from the police to become sadhus. After all, one hand cannot clap without the other.'

Grandfather had left home to become a monk. It was never mentioned in the house. One day, the boy stood behind the brass-studded door to his mother's bedroom as she lay dying. Grandmother sat by her bedside, holding Mother's frail, fair hand, which was veined with tributaries of blue. A slender gold bangle glinted on her wrist. Grandmother kept moving it up and down absent-mindedly.

'I could curse your father at times like these,' she was saying. Her voice was taut with anger, nevertheless stitched with an undertone of yearning. 'The rascal would be sitting under some tree in Benares, looking for god.'

'Maybe he found him, Amma,' his mother sounded far away, as if she was sitting with her lost father under the tree.

'It was the shame, daughter,' Grandmother said. 'When he ran away, people talked behind my back; they said it must have been my fault. After all, you can't clap with one hand they said.'

It was her favourite saying. He knew his mother's reply beforehand. 'It's no use having two hands and half a brain.'

This time, his mother didn't answer. Then he knew she was gone, having heard a wisp of a parting sigh that passed, caressing his face. He did not know his father. He was a tank commander who died in the 1965 war with Pakistan. It was the largest tank battle in history after World War II.

Sometimes Grandmother chose to bestow kindness on some itinerant monk. The boy suspected she hoped to hear news of her runaway husband; after all, sadhus travelled far and wide, moving from one place to another until they came to live in ancient holy cities like Benares, Haridwar, Rishikesh, Badrinath or in caves on the frosty slopes of the Himalayas.

These old sadhus were offered the hospitality of the outer veranda, where they sat gratefully in the shade of the tiled awnings. Their dusty sandals – some made of wood and some of cracked leather with heels fashioned from rubber taken from old tires – were kept discreetly beside the steps. The servants brought them leftovers from the kitchen. Grandmother watched the old monks eat; some muttering a hasty prayer before plunging into the milky mounds of rice mixed with lentils and buttermilk heaped on fresh, green banana leaves.

'How long have you been on the road?' she would ask some monk from her seat on the great wooden chair with brass armrests that used to be Grandfather's. 'Where all have you been?'

Many said they couldn't remember; they had been on the road for years. They spoke of miraculous sights they had seen and unimaginable dangers they had faced. They told of yogis who were thousands of years old and lived in the Himalayas. In a village in the northern mountains was a shivling that floated in the air. Anyone who touched it would be cured of disease, they said. In Tibet, they said, some monasteries kept immortal giant lizards to protect them from Chinese soldiers; one such lizard was the great Tibetan sorcerer Milarepa's pet. There were blind soothsayers in Kashi who could describe your face and predict your fate. There were monks who sat in crematoriums and conversed with the dead, binding their souls to bring them secrets of other men. It was a magical world, one the boy wanted to visit. He wanted to tell his grandmother all this, but somehow, he knew it wouldn't be received well.

The boy didn't know when the sadhu and his karma bull left. The next day, on his way home from school, he passed the Temple of a Thousand Bells. It had been a bad day. He had failed to do his math homework correctly. He carried the pain of the small red welt inside his curled fist where his teacher had caned him. When he was hurt about something, he always went to the temple and prayed, 'Om Namo Narayana, Om Nama Shivayah, make my pain go away. Make my path smooth.'

The temple was a small hexagonal structure made of ancient wood. Sooty little lamps, attached to black iron bands, encircled it. The roof was conical, crowned by a small flagpole. The temple was festooned with bells of all sizes; thousands of them. They covered the walls. Lines of bells on string were wrapped like garlands around the trunks of the banyan tree that cast its shade on the gravelled backyard. Bells were suspended from ropes that stretched from the flagpole to pillars sunk deep into the ground. People came from near and far. They tied bells wherever they could find space and whispered their wishes to the goddess who lived in the temple. When these were fulfilled, they came with more bells. Some didn't come back, but the bells they tied stayed where they were, part of the tinkling cacophony the monsoon winds made as they passed through the Palghat gap.

When the boy stepped onto the sandy temple courtyard, he saw the white bull tethered to the wish tree in the corner. It was lying down. Its owner was sleeping in the shade, his head resting on the bull. The boy turned around and tiptoed away, not to disturb his sleep. The sadhu called out, his eyes still closed. He held out a fist. The boy approached him warily.

'Don't be afraid, I have something for you,' said the sadhu. 'Here, open your fingers.'

The boy tentatively held out his palm. The sadhu placed a small manjadikuru on it, and closed it with his huge, dark fingers.

'Now open your hand again,' he said gently. The boy slowly opened his tightly clenched fist. There was a sudden flutter of wings and a small sparrow flew out from his palm, twittering. The boy felt no pain. The red welt was gone.

'Magic!' the boy whispered in wonder.

The sadhu nodded. 'It's the magic of your small god,' he said. 'Once you have found him, he will always be with you, protecting you.'

'Small god?'

'Yes, the small god looks after all the details of your life, things the big ones don't have the time for.'

'Will he be with me always?'

The sadhu nodded.

The boy looked at the great kind face, framed by the large white beard. He noticed the lines that ran deep on his forehead and his cheeks, and the wrinkles around his eyes and mouth. He realized that one day, he, too, would grow old like the sadhu or his grandmother. He shivered. The sadhu, as if divining the boy's fear, touched him lightly on his forehead. The boy felt immediately comforted. 'Thank you!' he said as he turned to leave, his palm tingling.

The sadhu nodded and went back to sleep. The boy didn't hear the soft words he muttered: 'God bless you, my grandson.'

A million temple bells pealed in the monsoon wind like blessings soaring on the wings of enchanted sparrows. They pealed across time and space, waking Asananda from his reverie, and he realized he was drifting along the Ganga's currents in Roopvati's silver boat. It was night. The chant of bells was coming from the sacred town faraway, accompanying the prayers that reverberated in the night.

Asananda reflected on the nature of journeys, realizing that not all of them were about moving forward; some were simply about waiting. He began to row towards the other shore, where the sheltering night waited for him at the end of the first day of his journey. He meditated on miracles.

The Monk Seeks the Small God

Asananda woke up to the arguments of birds. He looked around, startled, not knowing where he was. The morning was translucently dim. The sun had begun to clean the sky of stars. An irreproachable breeze caressed his face. Asananda could not recall when sleep had claimed him. Rowing had tired him. He had glimpsed an abandoned bathing ghat – one of the many that speckled the river's passage – and docked Roopvati's boat beside its stone steps. He had taken shelter under a large rosewood tree on the edge of the woods, which had almost taken possession of the white sand beach. He had spread his reed mat on a mossy, crumbling brick platform that encircled the tree. He always carried the mat, rolled up along with an old army issue horsehair blanket, when he travelled. Along with his satchel that contained a change of clothes and a small brass vessel with a spout, these were his only belongings. The sound of the boat grating against the steps as the river gently nudged it had lulled him to sleep.

When he awoke, his blanket was wet with dew and the boat was gone.

'O Narayana, yet another journey ends, leaving little behind of old lives,' he thought wryly. 'The Ganga subsumes everything.'

Asananda gingerly negotiated the broken steps and immersed himself in the cold embrace of the river. He looked up at the sky and bowed before the arriving sun, uttering the sacred words of the gayatri mantra eleven times. By the time he finished his ablutions, the morning had lit up the woods and young shadows gathered shyly on the underbelly of rock that cantilevered above like a giant's limb. On its edge, precariously, stood a ruined temple. A scraggly footpath ran uphill through the wild grass and bush.

Curious, Asananda took his possessions and walked up the path. It was a steep climb and his sarong often got caught in thistles and sharp mountain grass. A young cobra crossed his path, paused and raised its hood. Asananda folded his hands in reverence and waited for it to pass, since the serpent was Shiva's garland. The path ended in a long flight of narrow steps cut into rock, leading up. On top, the levelled ground was paved with large flagstones. The temple walls had crumbled into small mounds of grassy stone in most places. The monk passed through the broken doorway, feeling the cool mountain breeze carrying the scent of pine forests on his face. The roof of the temple's quadrangular colonnade had caved in. The wooden door that led to the sanctum lay askew in its frame. A man sat underneath a fig tree that grew in the middle of the courtyard.

'Om Ganeshaya namaha,' the man looked up and greeted Asananda. 'Om Vakratundaye namaha.' – Salutations to the Lord Ganesha, Salutations to the One with the Broken Tusk.

'Narayana, Narayana!' Asananda returned the greeting, folding his hands in a namaste. 'Did I disturb you?'

The man laughed. 'You cannot disturb me because I cannot sleep. I haven't slept in twenty years.' He wore a white cloth cap and an old brown shawl, patched and mended in places. He had bright brown eyes.

'How strange that you can't sleep,' Asananda said. 'Who are you?'

'I'm a passing storyteller, who makes a living by travelling from place to place telling wondrous tales,' the man said. 'Whenever I come this way, I climb up here to sit and reflect on the stories of the world and the characters and events that they are made of. Everyone is a story. God writes the stories of men, but the ones he blesses write their own. I just came to say goodbye to the Lord. He may be neglected, but that doesn't stop him from being the Lord. Now I'm on my way to the Himalayas.'

'Me too,' Asananda replied. 'I've quite a long journey ahead of me. I was curious about the temple, which is why I came to take a look.'

'As you can see, this is a Ganesha temple,' the storyteller said in a sonorous voice. 'It is just as well that you stopped here, since you say you are on a long journey.' He indicated the monk's meagre belongings. 'It is for the same reason I've come here, for the last time. What can be more auspicious than seeking the blessings of Lord Ganesha, Remover of Obstacles, when you are travelling?'

'I wish to reach Shivpuri by afternoon, so that I can spend the night at Devprayag,' the monk said.

'Bow to Ganesha and he will take you there unharmed,' the storyteller invited him.

Asananda looked doubtfully towards the stone grotto, inside which a wind-eaten idol, barely distinguishable as Ganesha but for its trunk, stood open to the elements. The storyteller smiled. He said, 'This is not a consecrated temple, since priests and devotees abandoned it years ago and no prayers have been offered here for decades. But it is a temple for the small god who lives everywhere.'

A childhood memory came to him with a jolt, of a sadhu with a white bull.

'What do you know about the small god?' Asananda whispered.

'All men who walk the road to the Himalayas know of the small god,' the storyteller answered. 'He is the god of solutions.'

'I've known about him from childhood. A long time ago, in another life, an ascetic asked me to seek my small god. But I had forgotten all about it.'

'The four-armed Ganesha always reminds you of forgotten blessings. With the goad in his upper right hand, he guides you forward on the eternal path. His broken tusk is the symbol of discarding the bad and retaining the good.'

'Did he help you find the small god?'

The storyteller nodded. 'Which is why I'm on my way to the Himalayas, to Mount Kailash, where Ganesha was born of Parvati and Shiva. I would worship at his feet, and immerse myself in the Mansarovar lake where Ganesha loved to bathe, and where all stories end. Stories are a burden, because they make up the memories of others, as well yours. If you tell them long enough, both become the same and you are living the karma of others. In Mansarovar, I will immerse all my stories and my burden will be over. And I can sleep at last.'

'That's good, because I'm also going to Kailash,' said the monk. 'But first, tell me how you found your small god.'

Without the help of the small god, Asananda knew he wouldn't be able to complete his task.

The Monk and the River Rider's Secret

'My name is Ramdhan and I was once a river rider,' the storyteller began.

He grew up in a village about a day's journey upriver from Rishikesh. His people were boat makers for generations, and his family was considered the best. In his grandfather's time, the king would commission royal barges from the family. The boatmakers lived in a small settlement by the Ganga, beside a vast beach of silver sand. Behind them, great green mountains stood guard; their peaks always bound with clouds that resembled torn pieces of floating muslin. Thick forests of pine and cedar shaped the lineaments of the mountainsides. Whenever the villagers got a fresh order for boats, they would take their children, along with mules bearing saws, axes and ropes, on woodcutting expeditions in the forest. The children were put in charge of the mules used to carry leftover pieces of chopped wood, dry branches and shears of timber to be used as firewood. The woodcutters loved having Ramdhan along because he had a melodious voice and knew many songs. The forest paths were narrow and got lost among the wild grass and the fronds. The climbs were often arduous.

The sound of furious mountain streams and waterfalls that fed the Ganga rumbled and thundered. Great trees shut out the sky in many places, casting an enchantment of pale green light. Little stone shrines to the gods of woodcutters dotted the path, and the children would light small lamps in the naves and pray for a good haul of timber and to return home unharmed by wolves and leopards. The villagers believed that Ramdhan's voice, being so sweet, would please the gods of the glades and keep harm away. Always, Ramdhan would be accompanied by two of his closest friends – the fair, muscular Puran, who was the son of the richest boatmaker in the village, and the golden-skinned Koyal.

After the trees were felled, the mules would haul the big logs towards the nearest mountain stream. The woodcutters would heave the timber into the frothy waters that toppled in over the shiny rocks. It was left to the strongest and most experienced boatmakers to retrieve the logs from the river, since it was a dangerous job. The logs would be seized with lassos thrown from rafts tied to grooves cut in the rock; the knot had to be perfect and the rope, new.

The rope thrower would swing a long underhand loop that rushed ahead to trap the oncoming timber from below, cutting a tail of spray through the rushing water. Sometimes when the tide was strong, the best swimmers among the villagers would leap into the galloping current to chase the careening logs and tie ropes around them. These would then be hauled ashore by waiting, cheering villagers. A little downstream from the shallow rapids, logs that escaped would be trapped in powerful nets made of hemp and iron wire, tied to poles driven into the riverbed. Then there were the young boatmakers who would leap on to the spinning, lurching logs to land gracefully on the shiny, wet wood, their supple bodies balanced by the forces of the wind and the currents, skilfully guiding the wood to the shore. They were called the river riders.

The river riders were special, and the villagers regarded them with respect and a bit of awe. They believed that the logs of the riders were actually gharials – the crocodile pets of the river Ganga. They knew that these creatures would never harm the river riders because they were the Ganga's children too. They would turn up on the beach to watch the ballet of the riders, cheering them on with whistles and waves. The women stood in a separate, colourful gaggle, following them with shining eyes and parted lips. Sometimes, a collective gasp would rise as a rider almost slipped off his log, followed by a silence so stark that the roar of the river seemed suddenly louder. After he righted himself, he would turn towards the little crowd, give an insouciant salute, and ride on, with the cheers of the villagers pursuing his swift course. Ramdhan was a river rider; one of the best.

He had learned to ride the logs when he was very young; barely fourteen. He was one of the gifted ones who could make a log of wood go wherever he wished, guiding it with his legs and the force of his body, playing with the wind and the tides to give him almost superhuman balance. He enjoyed the wind shaving his skin, and the river spray stinging his legs and feet as he felt the long smoothness of the wood under him move like a pitching, rolling river beast. Of all the river riders, the crowd loved him the most, and the women and young girls would gather around him, giggling and chattering, when he brought his log safely ashore. Ramdhan loved to race the river, and the precise moment the timber exploded on the sand and ploughed up the beach cleaving a wide furrow was when the world slowed and stopped for him. Then a sudden spray would shake him out of the silence, and his friend Puran would be beside him, calling his name and giving him congratulatory pats on his back.

Being a river rider was an art that could not be learned but only perfected. Timing was key; when to leap on top of the frenzied rolling, pitching, tilting block of wood and when to leap off. Riding the rapids was the worst part. Sometimes, the river rider would be hurtling towards the rocks and it took great skill to leap off the log and land on a tall, slick rock, spin without slipping on the ball of his feet as he followed the progress of his piece of wood with his eyes and again leap on to it as it cleared the churning water. Rarely, but once in many years, a river rider would fall and be swept away by the strong current; that night, great torches would be lit along the riverbank and there would be much feasting, singing and dancing – Mother Ganga has taken her favourite son, a soul who was born to salvation before the others.

One day, Ramdhan and Puran were sitting on the riverbank and fishing. They heard a cry and saw a speeding blur of clothes and flailing hands, being chased by a rushing log. Ramdhan suddenly found himself riding the log, crouching against the wind, which threatened to heave him off into the water. Later, stories were told around campfires, when the men sat drinking the heady brew of mountain flowers and palm sugar, about a boy who leaped on to a log to chase a drowning Koyal and grabbed her by the hair just as she was going to crash headlong into the rocks and lifted her up in his arms. With wonder, they had watched the log swim towards the bank, bearing Ramdhan and his beloved. Only when it crawled on to the beach did they see the glistening scales and the gaping jaws to realize that Ramdhan's log was really a gharial, the holy pet of the river goddess. None of the villagers had ever seen a river rider like that in their lifetime.

After that Koyal and Ramdhan became inseparable. Then on, Puran began to distance himself from them. He would shake off Ramdhan's hand from his shoulder when they met at the boatyard where they worked as apprentices. Puran would not meet his old friend's eyes when they passed one another; only when he saw Ramdhan and Koyal together would he glare at them with eyes ablaze with fury. Ramdhan's questions were only met with sullen silence. By the time they were old enough to become full-fledged boatmakers, with fuzz sprouting over their upper lips and chins, Puran had refused to work with Ramdhan. One day, Ramdhan was working on building a skiff, constructing its five ribs and attaching a pair of legs to each, while Koyal sat beside him chatting. A shadow fell over them, and Ramdhan looked up to meet Puran's fierce gaze. 'Leave her alone, Ramdhan,' he leaned over and hissed. 'She is mine. I have paid her father the bride price.'

Koyal gasped. 'I don't want to marry you,' she snapped. 'I'll die before I do that.' Puran's laugh was harsh.

'What is wrong with me? Am I not handsome? Isn't my face fair, unlike this monkey's?' he pointed towards Ramdhan. 'Aren't my arms strong and my chest broad? And I'm richer than him.'

Koyal stroked Ramdhan's suntanned cheek, 'But his heart is richer, and it is mine,' she said.

Puran tossed his head back, running his slender fingers through his shining black hair. The silver bangle on his wrist glinted like an omen.

'You've no choice, Koyal. Next spring, you will be mine. And Ramdhan here is too poor to afford a higher bride price.'

Koyal kicked sand into his face. He raised his hand to hit her, and Ramdhan was between them in a flash and had Puran by the throat.

After this incident, Koyal began to slowly withdraw into herself. Her eyes became dull, her face downcast and she hardly ever smiled. She would sit for hours by the riverbank, watching the water swirl by. One day, Ramdhan came and sat beside her.

'I've spoken to your father. He said he would not deny your hand to the most famous river rider anyone has ever known, but I would have to match Puran's bride price to marry you.'

Koyal gasped. 'How will you do that?'

'By building more boats than anyone else,' he said. 'I will work day and night to build more boats and better ones than anyone else. I am known as one of the best boatmakers in the village.'

From then on, the villagers saw Ramdhan always at work by the riverbank, constructing assembly frames, making cross planks and bottom runners, building and shaping stem pieces and smoothing out side panels. Even at night, they heard the sound of his hammer and chisel, and the scrape of his saw on timber. Sometimes, Koyal would go to sit beside him, watching him work and telling stories in her low, soft voice to amuse him.

Ramdhan painted the first boat he built silver. 'This boat is ours and, on our wedding night, we will row away in it. I've started saving money and, by next spring, I would have made enough to pay your bride price,' he told Koyal.

Ramdhan had built secret hollows in the planks and waterproofed them with tar. In these, he stored his money, and as months passed, Koyal's mood brightened. Ramdhan had found a small cave upstream beyond the bend in the Ganga, hidden behind the portiere of a waterfall and a tall pile of rocks. After dark, he would meet Koyal there, and they would lie in each other's arms and yearn for spring. Every night, as he rowed his silver boat to see her, he would sing soothing songs to the river. He sang half-remembered lullabies that asked the Ganga not to claim the boats the villagers made. From the distance, where the houses of rich merchants glowed like palaces of the gods, the strains of a tanpura would reach him, melodious and full of longing.

'Then one evening, I found my silver boat was gone, along with all my money,' the storyteller said. His voice was filled with a distant sadness, as though he was remembering the sorrowful end of some story he had once heard. 'And so was Puran. I quickly took another boat and rowed to the cave. There I found my Koyal dead, lying naked on the sand, her clothes ripped off and her skin shredded with nail marks. A silver bangle lay at a distance, and I recognized it as Puran's.'

'Did you find him?' asked the monk, half guessing the end of the story.

'He had disappeared along with my silver boat,' said the storyteller. 'I left the village, and became a wanderer. From that day, along with Koyal, sleep too left me. I had no more dreams left. I earned my living telling the stories Koyal used to tell me when I was building boats.'

The monk and the storyteller sat in the shade of the fig tree, looking out at the green valley through which the river flowed sedately, deep with centuries of stories. Beyond, the blue of the Himalayas was smoky with mist. The eroded idol of the elephant-headed god looked at them expressionlessly.

'This is where Koyal and I were to be married,' the storyteller told the monk. 'It was maintained by the boat keepers. Our villagers came here to pray, and so did many others from far away. We paid the priests and held our festivals here. Both at dawn and dusk, we could hear its bells pealing miles away. Once the lamps lit up Ganesha's face, his mischievous eyes would glitter. After Koyal was murdered and Puran disappeared, the villagers moved upstream where they established their home and built another temple. Ever since, this one has been abandoned. But not by me, as you can see.'

The monk was hungry. He spread his upper-cloth on the ground and sat cross-legged on it. From his pouch, he took out a frugal breakfast of bread, pickles and buttermilk, which the ashram cooks had packed before he started out.

'Would you like some buttermilk?' Asananda offered the storyteller. 'Your voice sounds dry, as if you are thirsty.'

The storyteller admitted he was. 'You are kind, sir,' he told the monk. 'But I cannot accept the buttermilk without giving you something in exchange. I could not earn any money today since there was nobody who wanted to listen to my tales. So all I can do, in return, is tell you a story.' The monk agreed. He did not have much use for money anyway. The storyteller drank the buttermilk in long, thirsty gulps. When he was finished, he turned to the monk and said, 'What sort of a story would you like to hear?'

The monk thought deeply. His guru had sent him on a journey to find the Book of Shiva. Gyanananda had told him that all journeys have secret codes that will open doors to reach god. Once the last door has been opened, man perceives god in his great majesty. This journey is called the path of meditation. But Asananda was tortured by the question: is it man who reaches god through meditation, or does god come to man? Does any story have a moral that explains this?

'I'm looking for the Book of Shiva,' he said. 'Do you know anything about it?'

'I don't know about the book, but I know a tale of Shiva and a quest,' the storyteller said. 'Perhaps it may help you.' He cleared his throat, spat a long plume of red betel juice on the ground, and started his narration.

The Monk Hears about the Lost Goddess

'Once upon a time, when the world was young, Lord Shiva's beloved wife Parvati wanted a new place to live in,' the storyteller began.

Shiva immediately plunged his trident into the ground and the earth cleaved into two, the seas split and the Himalayas rose out of the ocean bed. Shiva and Parvati chose Mount Kailash to live on. The Ganga lived in his tresses, flowing down to the plains, carrying his essence to the world. The newborn Mansarovar lake gleamed in the sun. Sometimes, Shiva and Parvati would dance through the night, coupled in divine yoga, and their lovemaking made Ganga jealous.

'I am the one closest to him,' she thought. 'I caress his tresses as I gush out, I hear his thoughts before they are formed. I feel the coldness of his intellect and the heat of his desires. I wash his skin and perfume his face. Yet he does not acknowledge my love.'

One day, when Parvati went down to bathe, Ganga sent a huge wave that carried her away. Shiva searched for his wife everywhere.

'Why do you look for her when you have me?' Ganga asked. 'I have taken her to my depths, where Yama, the God of Death, lives.'

'What have you done?' Shiva screamed in despair. He dived into the river, deeper and deeper, until he reached Yama's abode. He pounded on the door of skulls, which shook under the rage of his fists. Hearing the commotion, Yama came out. Seeing the master of the universe, he bowed.

'My lord, if you have come for your wife, it is useless,' said Death. 'No one can return from the land of Yama. It is the law of karma.'

Shiva wept and pleaded, bribed the God of Darkness with war and pestilence, but Yama was unmoved. Shiva became angry. He took Death by the throat and snarled. 'I will open my third eye and you and your dark land will become cinders in an instant,' he thundered, 'return Parvati to me.'

'It is against the rules of the universe,' Death pleaded. 'There is no looking back once a soul reaches me.'

'Then think of a way out, or I will finish you and your rules,' threatened Lord Shiva.

Death bowed his head in thought. After a while, he looked up at his lord.

'I have thought of a way,' he said. 'You walk away from here and I will send Parvati after you. But whatever you see, hear or feel, you will not look back until both of you reach the top of Mount Kailash. If you break this covenant, you will lose her forever.'

Shiva agreed. He set out towards the Himalayas. 'Can you see Parvati?' he asked a passing lark.

'Yes, my lord,' the bird replied, 'she is walking right behind you.' He strained his ears to hear the footfalls of his beloved, but they were as soft as a shade's. He knew he could not look back.

After walking for a while, he asked a doe that had come down to drink from a mountain stream, 'Can you see Parvati?'

'Yes, my lord, she is just a few paces behind you,' the doe said, gazing at him with soft, dark eyes.

Shiva walked on, restless to see his beloved, take her soft, fair body in his arms and kiss her warm, red lips. As he climbed up the path that led to the mountaintop, he asked a passing leopard if Parvati was behind him.

'Yes, my lord, right behind you,' the big cat said, gracefully springing away on its long powerful legs.

As he crested the last ridge, Shiva in his eagerness quickened his steps. His stride dislodged a stone, sending it rolling down. Shiva heard a soft gasp and Parvati cry out his name. In consternation, he turned around and saw his wife fall, hit by the stone. Too late, he realized his mistake, and Yama appeared riding his great, black buffalo and carried Parvati away into the netherworld.

In a rage, Shiva opened his tresses and Ganga fled, thundering down the Himalayan slopes, crushing smaller mountains and rocks in its path until she spread over the plains and found refuge in the ocean.

'May you nourish the earth forever and cover it with meadows and gardens that Parvati loved, but you will be always full of rotting corpses, dead animals and decaying trees,' Shiva cursed Ganga. 'Men will drown their sins in you, and children will throw the ashes of their fathers that are tainted with their sins. You will be full of sin, and to cleanse yourself of your own sin, you will flow forever.'

The storyteller finished.

'What happened to Parvati?' the monk asked.

'Her son Ganesha brought her back from the land of Yama,' replied the storyteller. 'But that is another story. This is the only one I have for you.'

From the broken courtyard of the ruined temple on the hill, Asananda looked towards the Ganga; its dun-coloured water seemed sluggish and sorrowful. 'One who cleanses oneself with the sins of others? What a paradox karma is,' the monk thought.

'Did you ever look behind you for Koyal?' he asked the storyteller.

'No, I don't have to, she is always with me,' the man replied. 'It is better not to look back at the past because then you won't be able to see what the future has to offer you.'

The monk stood up and picked up his belongings.

'I have a long way to go,' he said. 'But before I leave, I must ask you whether you have found the small god.'

The storyteller pointed with his chin towards Ganesha.

'I have found mine, the one who brought Parvati back from the land of Death,' he said. 'Each person has his or her own small god, who belongs only to them.'

A strong gust of breeze shook the fig tree and dislodged pale golden leaves that fell on the storyteller like random words of grace.

The Monk and the Desperate Sinner

The afternoon was fading by the time the monk left Shivpuri behind on his way to Devprayag. From there, he could push further on to Nandaprayag and Joshimath, and onwards to the snowy peak of Mount Kailash, where Lord Shiva lived. He would bathe in the turquoise waters of the Mansarovar lake that lay at the foot of the mountain. Its waters are believed to transport the devotee's soul to Shiva. Asananda did not know how long it would take to reach the mountain and find the Book of Shiva. He wasn't even sure it would be there; his master had been delightfully vague about it. 'You never know, Asananda,' Gyanananda had chuckled, 'seek and ye shall find, or be found.'

'So it's back to cause and effect? Because there is a quest, a book can be found, or is it because there is a book to be found, there is a quest?' Asananda had asked in exasperation. 'It confuses me.'

The master had laughed, his potbelly shaking with merriment. He placed a gentle hand on his disciple's shoulder.

'Have faith, it is the best weapon to dispel confusion,' Gyanananda said. 'Without faith, how will you realize your dream?'

'What is faith, master?'

'Faith is divine optimism, Asananda. That there is forgiveness for the worst sinner.'

'Forgiveness of god?'

'That, too. But ultimately, to forgive oneself is to set oneself free.'

The monk smiled at the memory and quickened his steps. An owl hooted in the woods. The rough music of mountain streams softened and spread in the wind. The Himalayas were a dreamy blue, at a wistful distance, which called out to the monk. His eyes filled with tears. Wiping his wet cheeks, Asananda passed below a serrated hillside whiskered by fronds. Ahead, he glimpsed a small shrine built against a rock at an elevation. Steps cut into the rock face led up to it from the roadside. He bowed his head respectfully in passing to whichever deity resided within. With a start, he realized that he had prayed to the small god that his steps would take him in the right direction.

'Swamiji, please stop,' someone hailed him from behind.

The monk looked back. A woman was standing on the steps, her hand raised in a plea. She was short and fair, with a round face. She wore a blue sari patterned with summer flowers, the vermillion evident in the parting of her curly hair. When she came close, the monk noticed she had a coarsely voluptuous body, but a face deeply lined by some secret sorrow. The monk sat down on a cement bench on the roadside. The woman came and sat beside him. Her eyes shone with anticipation, the pupils enlarged as if she had put belladonna in them. Asananda raised his eyebrows in interrogation.

'O sanyasi, I seek absolution,' she said in a harsh, pleading voice. 'Not for myself, for I am beyond redemption, but for my son who is lost. I know all yogis can see the future and the past and know pujas that can cleanse bad karma. If my son's sin is forgiven, god will return him to me.'

Asananda was puzzled. 'Your son must be a child. What sin has he committed that frightens you so?' he asked.

'His sin is that he was born to me. I once heard a sermon by a holy man who said that we come into this world to suffer and expiate the sins of our past life.'

'I don't know about that. What has happened to him?' Asananda asked. 'Where is he?'

She began to sob.

'I don't know. It has been a week since he disappeared. I've been looking for him everywhere, in his school, in the playground, at bus stands and railway stations. The last I saw of him was when he was going to school. He looked so beautiful, his uniform starched and pressed, his curly hair oiled and slicked back and his cheeks like fresh apples. He kissed me and asked me to make plantain curry for dinner. He loved it. Where is my son now, swamiji?'

Asananda felt both embarrassed and saddened. He confessed that he had no clue to the future and the past, which should be left to astrologers. He was just a monk on his way to Kailash.

'As my son was leaving, a sadhu came to my house seeking alms,' she said. 'And I gave him money and asked my boy to touch his feet. The sadhu even blessed him. How can someone blessed by god in the morning vanish forever?'

Asananda knew that sadhus are as flawed as other men, because they, too, were just men. He kept the thought to himself to avoid distressing the woman further.

'I even went to the morgue to look,' she shuddered. 'I saw a little child who had drowned. It wasn't him. I felt happy that it wasn't my son, but I wept for his mother. Mothers are like that.'

Unable to help the unfortunate woman, Asananda felt sad. But she persisted. She said, 'You are a yogi and therefore can tell the past and the future.'

'I cannot do either, sister,' Asananda said. 'But I'm sure god will return him to you.'

'God is angry with me, for tainting my son with my sin,' she said forlornly. 'You see, I am married, but my son is by my lover, who was a mountain guide from my village. He was a handsome, sturdy man who seduced me with stories about his travels to the Himalayas, taking white tourists on treks to glaciers, and the money he earned. He would charm me with anecdotes of hermits and mountain gods, and battling sakus – tigers that ate only the flesh of wild horses. There is nothing like danger that attracts a woman and make her behave foolishly. One day, he went on an expedition to Badrinath and never returned. My husband didn't know I was pregnant by my lover. But whenever I watch him shower my child with love, believing he is the father, I burn with guilt.'

The monk did not know how to help this troubled mother.

'Where is your husband? If he loves the boy so much, why isn't he with you, looking for him?' he asked.

'He left me,' she said, hanging her head. 'I confessed. I will never forget the look on his face as long as I live. His eyes looked like wounds.'

Asananda spread his palms out helplessly.

'Don't you see, my sin haunts this child?' she said fiercely. 'It is the reason he is lost. Perhaps his father's shade stole him. Perhaps both are now ghosts, wandering in the mountains or the Valley of Flowers, guiding dead mountaineers.'

The monk closed his eyes and had a vision of endless snow that segued into the sky, forming a great cupola lit by a cold, silver sun. He saw the mountains as a great calligraphy of ice and white rock, and the glaciers and frosty rivers were a part of the gigantic Himalayan landscape. He squeezed his eyes tight, disturbed by the fragment of an old vision; of two sets of footprints – one large, the other small, side by side, tattooing the path through the blinding whiteness. Father and son in the endless snow – a vision, warm and distant, which filled his heart with longing.

The woman broke into tears. 'I have sinned, and god has punished me by making my boy vanish,' she sobbed. 'Can't you do a puja to purify my karma seeking god's forgiveness, which will return him to me?'

'Perhaps it is god who makes people sin,' Asananda said, 'as much as he makes them do good. Sin may be a test to make us realize how weak we are.'

The woman did not look convinced about a god who made people do both right and wrong. She threw her hands up in exasperation. Her glass bangles clinked.

'So will you do a puja for my son or not? How many rupees will you charge?'

The monk shook his head in regret.

'At least tell me what to do,' she pleaded.

'Someone once told me that the small god was the god of solutions. Maybe you should pray to him.'

'In which temple do I find him? Will he forgive my sin?'

'You do not wish to be free of sin, but only of guilt,' he said. 'You feel your torment is enough of a bribe to let god forgive you.'

The woman looked nonplussed for a moment. He watched her turn and wearily walk back to the shrine, climb the steps and collapse on the stone floor of the veranda. The monk shook his head sadly and walked on. If it was so easy, he thought, if a few hired prayers could clean up karma, then god would be running a supermarket.

Asananda did not know any pujas, rituals or the Vedas. He did not even know the correct yoga pose for meditation. He did not know the arcane gestures to make as his voice spelt out ancient, powerful words. He did not know which flowers were offered to which god. All he knew was that when he sat down, closed his eyes and felt gentle and even friendly with god, the arcane words and gestures came automatically. He did not have to forget. He didn't have to remember either. It was a gift he had received from his master.

Asananda thought about the distraught woman he had left behind. He wished he could have given her the gift of peace, the words to quieten her restless soul. But only masters could do that and he was not one. Until she found the one to free her, she, like so many others who sought to calm their tortured hearts, would wander in sorrow.

When he was wandering the Himalayas, sheltering in caves inhabited by wild animals that, miraculously, did not harm him, and sleeping under ancient trees that stood along the old caravan route to Tibet, he would wonder about the scheme of things that made him a wanderer. What sin was he trying to shed on the snow? What guilt was he trying to wash away in the freezing mountain streams before he found, again, the hand of the Great Father?

It was so long ago since he had left the snow and ice behind. It seemed like another lifetime. The war was so long ago. Asananda remembered standing guard at the Kaksar range army outpost. His comrades were inside their bunkers, huddled around a small gas stove. It was his watch. Icicles had formed on the roof of the bunkers. All around him was an endless domain of ice and snow. He remembered hearing a slap that cracked across the thin air, followed by the booming of guns. He remembered the surprise of falling. He heard thunder and, as he fell, he saw dark figures floating towards him. Shells from the heavy 150 mm artillery guns were exploding on the snow everywhere, creating huge spidery cracks in the ice. One bunker was on fire. The destroyed concrete muffled the screaming that came from inside. Behind him, the Indian guns opened up. He lay on his back in the snow, looking up at mortar shells streaking across the sky. He felt no pain. He was dreaming.

In the vision, a gigantic soldier was kneeling down beside him. The giant leaned over and whispered something. He realized that it was not a soldier at all. He gazed up in wonder at the great face that regarded him with eyes bluer than the Himalayan lakes guarded by glaciers, from under charcoal-black brows. Fine silver fur, the colour of fresh snow on a cloudless afternoon, covered the face. The red mouth was slim and long. He was filled with a deep sense of safety he had never experienced before. The harsh howl of the Himalayan winds subsided to a soothing hum. It was like a chant heard in childhood, at the time when temples opened their doors and the gods awoke. He felt the being's great arms gather him and their limitless strength that had borne mountains, forests and sacred herbs. He snuggled up to the warm chest and closed his eyes.

'Rest, my son,' he heard a deep voice that seemed to surround him like ocean, like ice, like the wind. 'I am the Primordial Father and you have come home to me.'

He passed into a darkness that muffled him like a soft cloth. When he woke up days later in the field hospital, he felt different. He was someone else. He liked the person.

The rumble of a bus turning a corner on the road broke the monk's reverie. It passed, farting billows of black diesel fumes as its dilapidated body fought gravity uphill. Asananda covered his face with cloth, coughing. He glimpsed faces of passengers, bored expressions of people who were taking a familiar, monotonous, journey. Among these, like a pale wafer of skin showing against a cloud of dark hair, was the face of the woman who sought her bastard son. She briefly turned to look at him, and then her face disappeared in a huge, odious cloud of smoke. He silently begged her forgiveness, and hoped she would have found the peace she so desperately sought the next time they met. If they ever met again. Something told Asananda he would see her once more.

The Ganga escorted Asananda as he walked, a brown torrent that abruptly thinned out in places, and picked up farther away, hurling itself on stubborn clumps of rock in a tumult of froth and spray.

'Om namo Narayana,' he sighed. 'Om namo Shivayah. Let her journey end well, and mine, too.'

The Monk and the Yogi in the Cave

Asananda reached the sacred town of Devprayag at dusk. He had hitched a ride on a jeep, which let him off at the side of the road that formed a girdle around the hill as it climbed. He looked down the gorge towards the frothy tumult of the prayag, the point where the quiet blue river, Alaknanda, met the tempestuous brown Bhagirathi, as they rushed down the Himalayas to form the Ganga. From there, the great river begins its journey to the Bay of Bengal. The town got its name from the prayag.

Darkness condensed softly on the conical hills above Devprayag, permeating the conifer and sal trees, while the mountain ranges afar remained gilded with the remains of the day. The hillside formed a sweeping crescent along the Alaknanda. Ashrams, homes, hotels and shops tumbled down towards its table-shaped shore, framed by large rocks. Steps led down to a grey stone platform at the prayag. The monk could see the white cupola of the giant stone temple of Raghunath glowing in the deepening dusk. Someone in a village somewhere was playing a dhol, and the beats of the drum swayed and tossed in the wind. Asananda decided not to seek shelter in any of the ashrams. He wanted to spend the night beside the river, listening to its ancient sutra and meditate on the small god.

Who was he? Where does one find him? And will he lead him to the Book of Shiva?

Asananda recalled hearing about a riverside cave in Devprayag from his master, and the many great ascetics and sadhus who had meditated and practised austerities there. He peered down the incline. No road led down the steep slide to the white strip of beach below; it was a precarious descent to where the Ganga made a wide half-moon and then flowed on.

Recalling the master's directions, he gingerly trod his way through rocks and pebbles that interrupted the vast sweep of sand, looking for the cave. The sound of temple bells tripped along in the wind. After exploring for a while, he found a narrow vertical split in the rock, through which he could see only serene darkness beyond. The monk squeezed through the crack. As he felt his way along a tunnel that seemed to go on forever, the noise of the Ganga slowly faded into the darkness. Moving forward, he heard soft breathing. As his eyes adjusted to the gloom, Asananda found that he was standing in a small alcove. In the darkness, he saw the outline of a shivling and the dim gleam of a trident. Against the wall, almost looking like a fresco, sat a yogi in the lotus position, deep in meditation. The air was fragrant with incense. Asananda felt a great peace blessing him. He lowered himself down on the floor, which was paved with fine sand. He leaned back against the mossy wall of the cave and closed his eyes. He felt the astral presence of the hundreds of ascetics who had meditated here, their spirits leaving their austere, emaciated bodies at the moment of awakening and soaring away towards the Great Solace.

'Welcome my son,' a soft voice addressed him. A match flared in the darkness, its light pencilling a brown hand that stretched out to light a lamp, which illuminated large, deep eyes, an abundance of white beard and a face framed by dreadlocks. On the yogi's forehead, a crimson sign was drawn vertically across a thick smear of sandal paste. It looked like an all-seeing third eye. Asananda folded his palms.

'Where am I? Is this the cave my master told me about?' he asked. The yogi's eyes twinkled mischievously.

'I'm just an ascetic who has been living here for many years, meditating on the meaning of life and death. I hope one day I will find it.'

'In this cave?'

'Why not? Isn't it as much a part of the world as a house or an inn? There is meaning everywhere, for everything. The world is a vast mirage of meanings. If god smiles on you, he may show you the exact meaning you seek. But what do you seek, my son?' the holy man asked.

'The Book of Shiva. Before that, the small god.'

'You cannot find one without the other.'

'Is the small god inside this cave?'

'This cave itself is not easily found. Only those who are summoned are led here.'

'Who summoned me?'

The yogi did not answer. He stood up. Inside the cave, by lamplight, his shadow hovered over the monk like a gigantic angel. He addressed Asananda: 'You know that every journey leads through many gates. Beside every gate is a guardian, waiting with a message. There is a lesson in each message. A toll is extracted, which may cause both pain and sorrow, or give great joy and freedom. But at the end of each lesson, you reach one step closer to what you are looking for.'

'Am I to understand that this cave is a gate and you are its guardian? What is your message?'

The yogi did not answer. He turned towards the cave's entrance and beckoned Asananda to follow. They strolled along the darkening Ganges. Night floated its shadows in the water, which gathered in the crevices of rocks in its way. The edges of rocks were beaten white with river froth. Lights were coming on in the holy town of Devprayag above, illuminating the sundry buildings heaped on the riverbank. The opera of prayers from ashrams and temples rose and fell in the night. Ancient psalms melded with the clapping of myriad hands, the sounds soaring and then fluttering away like crowds of doves.

'Where are we going?' the monk asked the yogi.

'To a place where the small god lives.'

They walked towards a hill, which sloped down into the river. As they climbed along the small path that led up from the bank of the Ganga, Asananda could see smoke emanating from top of the hill. A fiery glow lit the atmosphere. They reached the plateau of the hilltop. Innumerable fires were burning everywhere. Asananda realized they had reached a cremation ground.

'You mean the small god lives in a funeral ground?' Asananda asked incredulously. 'This is morbid.'

'He is everywhere,' the yogi answered. 'Have patience. Without patience, how can you find god?' He laughed. He looked vaguely familiar. Asananda racked his brains, but the memory lingered beyond the edges of his mind.

Concrete benches lined the long, crumbling wall around the charnel ground. The yogi sat down on one and signalled to Asananda to sit beside him. They sat in silence, watching corpses burn. A man was hobbling among the pyres, poking at the burning wood and pushing errant logs back in with a stout stick.

'He is the keeper of the cremation ground,' said the yogi. He hailed him. The keeper approached them, his face and body dark with the soot of the dead. Their ash clung to his matted hair and unkempt beard, and mingled with the soot. He squatted on the ground, which was paved with bricks, took out a beedi and lit it. The yogi stood up.

'I've to get going now but I brought him here to meet you,' the yogi said told the man. 'He wants to find his small god.'

The charnel keeper looked at Asananda with calm, wounded eyes. 'Do you know the story of Harischandra, the king who had never uttered a single lie and lived in a cremation ground?'

The monk vaguely remembered the story. Harischandra was a king who only spoke the truth and believed in keeping his word. He had a beautiful wife whom he was devoted to. They didn't have a child, and god granted them a boy on the condition that he would be returned as sacrifice. This was to test the strength of the king's word. Later, the king was forced to give up his kingdom and sell his wife and child to a Brahmin. He became a servant of Yama, who was disguised as a charnel keeper. One day, when his wife brought their dead son to the cremation ground, he asked her for payment since it was his duty as the keeper. All she had was the sari she was wearing. She gave Harischandra half of it. The gods, pleased by his integrity, brought the king's son back to life and restored his kingdom to him.

'I've never liked that story,' Asananda said. 'It's too one-sided. Harischandra had to suffer for something that was not his fault.'

'Oh, but it was,' said the charnel keeper. 'His fault lay in his ego, which compelled him to keep his word, no matter what it cost those he loved. Even in his darkest moments, it was his ego that comforted him.'

'Then why were the gods pleased with him?' asked Asananda.

'It was his wife they were pleased with, because she was willing to sacrifice all that she was left with for her son's sake. On her son's pyre, she was willing to burn her ego and pride.'

Asananda pondered over this.

'The ego makes even the ones you love suffer,' the charnel keeper said. 'The cremation ground is where all egos end. Here, everyone burns to ashes; the rich and the poor, the mighty and the weak, the young and the old, women and children. I throw their remains into the Ganga, which receives them all with the purity of death.'

'How long have you been doing this?' asked Asananda.

'A long time,' the charnel keeper said. 'I was once a businessman, and I too had a beautiful wife and a son we loved very much.'

Another story, Asananda sighed. How many more are there on this road? Yet he knew deep within that all of them contained meanings that would eventually come together to show him the way to the Book of Shiva.

The Monk in the Charnel House

The keeper of the charnel house inherited his father's business when he was young. He was a crafty businessman, and knew how to cut a clever deal. Soon he became rich and even richer as time passed. He was proud of his cleverness. But he was always afraid that his riches would be stolen. He donated generously to temples so that god would prevent this from happening. He even built temples in gratitude to god for having made him rich. As his wealth grew, so did his pride. Money was his only love, and he neglected his wife and son. When his wife fell ill, he employed the best doctors, but he was so busy making money he did not have any time to spend with her. When she died, he was in Bombay, buying land for a new factory. He couldn't even attend the funeral and it was his son who cremated her.

When he returned home, his son would not speak to him. The servants told him that the boy was refusing to eat or drink, and spent long hours staring into space. The next day, he disappeared. The businessman was distraught. He spent huge amounts of money on private detectives and bribing the police. The boy couldn't be found.

The businessman devoted all his energies into making more money, because it had now become a solace. He built more factories, bought and sold businesses and became a multimillionaire. Many years passed. One day, while he was upstairs in his room, checking the stock prices on his computer, the doorbell rang. A young man stood outside, whom the millionaire immediately recognized as his son. His first instinct was anger, but the handsome young man cut such a fine figure that the father felt his chest swell with pride.

'What a fine son I have,' he told himself, clasping the young man to his breast. The millionaire asked his servants to serve the young master food and drink. He sat with the young man as he ate, listening to his story.

After the boy left home, he boarded a train to Delhi. There he worked many menial jobs, including as a waiter in a small restaurant. One day, he pointed out to a regular customer that the restaurant owner was overcharging him. The owner became angry and sacked him on the spot. But the customer, a small-time businessman, was impressed with the boy's honesty and hired him. Soon the young apprentice proved to possess an astute business sense. In a few years, he built up the business so much that he was made a partner – the youngest one in the firm's history. A few years later, he had made enough money to buy the owner out. And here he was, at his father's door, having proved himself.

'My heart swelled with pride and my ego became even bigger,' said the charnel keeper. 'All the good work I had done for god had given me a fine son. The next day, I inducted him into the business.'

The young man proved his worth after a few months on the job, cutting quick deals and making decisions that were financially sound and profitable. Soon he expanded the business, opening more outlets and finding new partners willing to put in their money. One day he urged his father to go on a pilgrimage; after all, the old man had been working without a break for so many decades and needed a holiday. The millionaire reluctantly set out. But as weeks passed and he stopped and worshipped at all the temples he had wished to but couldn't find the time for, he began to feel calm and happy like never before. His son would call often and tell him that business was booming.

One day when the millionaire was in the holy town of Guruvayoor, he went to the ATM and found, to his surprise, that there was no money in his account. He thought it was a mistake. He phoned his son, but his calls went unanswered. He called both his trusted accountant and secretary who had been with him for decades, and they told him that they had been sacked soon after he left. He returned home immediately and went straight to the office from the airport. He learnt that most of his companies had gone under and the banks were foreclosing on them. Even his office building was mortgaged. His son had ruined in five months what he had built up in five decades. The millionaire was full of rage – towards his son and the gods on whom he had spent so much money. He rushed home and found policemen milling around the house. They had come for his son. They informed him that the young man was a known swindler. The old servant broke down when she saw her master – she had been the son's ayah when he was a small child – and led him upstairs. The millionaire's son lay dead in his room on the first floor. He had shot himself. It was his final revenge. He had also left behind a suicide note, which said, 'Now, Father, how does it feel to lose everything?'

'I brought him here. I cremated him myself. As I sat by his pyre and watched the flames turn into coals, and then into ash, I felt strangely free. My ego had burnt down with my son's body, and so had the rest of my life. I haven't left since,' the charnel keeper finished his narrative.

The monk got up and walked slowly among the pyres, pausing at times to gaze thoughtfully at the burning bodies. Suddenly he stopped. On a stack of wood, illuminated by the fires, lay the body of a young woman dressed in a blue sari patterned with summer flowers. Her long eyelashes rested on her round cheeks. A cloud of curly hair framed her face, which was swollen and turning blue. The fire of the biers around sputtered and blazed as a cold gust of wind swam across the river. Asananda shivered. The charnel keeper came up to him.

'She was fished out of the river this evening,' he said. 'She must have drowned. Since nobody seems to know her, I decided to cremate her myself.'

'I know her,' Asananda said, 'she came to me for absolution.'

'Did you give it to her?'

'No. It's a long story. In the end, I see that the Ganga has given it to her.'

'We bear our sins so lightly that we are not even aware of them; a good reason why they keep multiplying. But guilt, when it comes, is too much to bear. The Ganga has cleansed her sins, and the fire will purify her,' the charnel keeper said. He began to stack wood over the woman's body.

'May I light her pyre?' the monk asked.

The charnel keeper lit a piece of wood from a burning pyre nearby and handed it to the monk. Asananda circled the young woman's bier, firing the wood that covered the body. He watched the flames spread until the pile became a bonfire. He stepped away from the sudden blast of heat.

'What did you tell her when she met you?' the charnel keeper asked Asananda after a spell of silence.

'To pray to the small god.'

'Did you teach her how to? If you had, perhaps she may not have ended up here.'

'How could I,' asked Asananda in despair, 'when I haven't found him myself?'

The charnel keeper bade him to sit on an empty concrete platform, meant for placing biers. 'You need to lose everything to find the small god,' he said. 'Everyone prays to god, in good times and bad, pleading for help or expressing gratitude. At times, when they feel their prayers are not heeded, they curse god and call him names. They rave and rant. But as in everything else, the scholars will tell you there is a hierarchy in prayer too. First, pray to yourself before you pray to god.'

Asananda was taken aback.

'Yes, the first prayer of the day should be to yourself. That you may give yourself the strength to face the troubles ahead, and thank yourself at night that you were strong enough. Pray to yourself that you are able to forgive yourself for actions done in anger or haste, and for hurt caused and betrayals done, for it is easier to forgive others than forgive oneself. You should pray to yourself that you may have the power and conviction to protect and defend those you love and the will to face those who mean you harm. You should pray to yourself for the strength to believe in yourself. And also for strength to believe in god. You yourself are the small god.'

The wind that danced over the funeral grounds brought with it the wisdom of the ancient souls who live in the Himalayas. It caressed the flames that consumed the dead. The moon lazed behind a length of cloud, and night glowed with fireflies and scattered the starry sky as a shimmering vestment on the flowing river. The mountains crouched in the mist and the darkness, heavy with secrets and danger. The monk gazed towards the mountain across the river, where the yogi's cave was. Along the shining sand of the riverbank, he saw something large and white. It was moving slowly. A distant but clear tinkling of bells sculled in the wind. Like a revelation, the moon flooded the night and Asananda saw clearly a white Brahma bull being led by a familiar figure. Even from the distance he could make out the saffron clothes and the long, matted hair. The yogi paused and waved. The moon disappeared as suddenly as it had come, and the night was embroidered with the dance of the fireflies. A guardian had left, after leading him to the end of a lesson that started on a childhood afternoon in the distant past. And he had neither recognized nor thanked the one who showed him the first miracle of his life.

The monk felt his eyes sting, and a sob filled him like fresh spring water. He prayed to the small god for the strength to complete his quest in the tempests of the other lessons that awaited him. All around, the myriad flames kept up their mysterious chatter of wasted prayers.

The Monk and the Man Who Did Not Understand Money

Asananda woke up hungry. It was almost dawn, and the sky was rent by glowing fissures of yellow and orange, which reminded him of funeral fire. The charnel keeper had offered him the hospitality of his small hut. Since it was late, Asananda had accepted and shared a bowl of rice and dal with him.

Asananda went to look for his host, but he was nowhere to be seen. Most of the pyres had burned down, and it was too early for relatives to come and collect the bones for immersion. A part of the Ganga sutra – the prayer to the holiest of rivers – written by the ancient devotional poet Tulsi Das came to his mind.

Gange mamagratho bhooya, gange may devi prushtadha,
Gange may parswayorehi, thwayi gangesthu may sthithi.

'O river Ganga, appear ahead of me as well as behind me,
O river Ganga, appear alongside me on both sides,
O Ganga, allow me to be a part of you.'

The monk washed and brushed his teeth with the twig of a margosa tree he carried in his satchel. He wanted to leave behind something as a token of gratitude to the charnel keeper. He searched in his bag for the rosary made of one hundred and eight utrasas – or rudraksha beads – that helped him keep count while reciting his prayers. Legend says utrasa beads are formed from the teardrops of Shiva, which fall to the earth from Mount Kailash, as he weeps for the sorrows of mankind. He kept it on the floor of the hut as he left, muttering a prayer. He hoped the tears of Shiva would purify the charnel keeper's sorrow that made him toil among the burning dead, which reminded him of his son every time he cared for a funeral pyre – keeping the stray dogs away and ensuring that the wood burned properly, and the bones and ashes of the unclaimed were collected in urns of clay and thrown into the Ganga after the necessary rituals were completed.

'I don't need a rosary, I remember all my prayers and mantras. It's just a habit,' Asananda told himself. 'And habits, good or bad, only tie you down further to the world. The tears of Shiva will at least purify my host's penance.'

Asananda remembered asking his guru once, 'When does one stop needing things?'

'Only when one has everything,' Gyanananda had replied.

'When does one know one has everything?'

'When you know you do not need anything, for then you have everything because everything is unnecessary.'

As he left the funeral ground with his satchel, staff and begging bowl, he felt gratitude towards his master. Devprayag was waking up. Even at dawn, people walked along its tiny street, alone or in groups, to bathe in the little enclosures built along the Ganga. They were on their way to temples and halls where bhajans and discourses were on, or were just starting. Asananda chose a stone platform beside a bathing ghat with steps leading down to the river, spread his folded reed mat and sat down to beg. He did not plead or ask for money; he simply kept his brass bowl in front of him. People were used to seeing sadhus begging by the roadside; so few paid him any attention. Some tossed a few coins into his bowl. He noticed a woman pass him, slow her steps, and then walk on. Her husband walked cockily in front. He was a tall, immensely fat man wearing a brown chikan kurta and dazzling white cotton pajamas. He wore a small square moustache under his nose. His face was coarse-skinned. He was probably a merchant from a small town, the monk thought; from Uttar Pradesh, maybe. He saw the woman return, cross him and again pause before walking on. When she passed him for the third time, the monk smiled at her. She smiled back tentatively. She was dressed in a crisp cotton sari. It was purple, with patterns of intertwined vines and a deep green border. She had soft eyes and greying hair. She wore a huge red bindi and a smear of vermillion powder above it. Noticing that his wife had stopped by Asananda, the merchant muttered something rude under his breath. The monk caught the words, 'dirty thief'. The morning light broke over the holy town, gilding the towers and flag staffs of temples. The tolling and tinkling of temple bells eddied in the air. The wind held the faint fragrance of incense, mixed with the crisp smell of river water.

The woman fumbled in her bag. 'Here, holy man,' she said in a low, trembling voice. 'Take this money and bless me and my family.'

She bent down and placed a hundred rupees in a small black bowl made of dried gourd, which was kept beside the monk. There were a few coins in the bowl. The monk picked up the rupee note and held it out to her.

'Om namo Narayana! I'm grateful for your kindness,' he said. 'But all I need is a rupee.'

The merchant came over and joined her. She looked confused and anxious. The husband said in a surprisingly squeaky voice for such a fat man, 'That's all you get, you greedy beggar. Now get lost.' He took his wife by the arm to lead her away, but she shook it off. The monk still had his hand out, with the money clutched in his fingers. The woman snapped at her husband, 'He doesn't want hundred rupees. He only wants one rupee.'

The man, who was getting ready to abuse the monk further, was startled. His jaw dropped. His eyes bulged.

'What sort of a joke is this? Don't you dare make fun of me, or else ...'

'Just give me a rupee,' the monk said.

'Listen, I am a very rich man. So take the hundred rupees and thank god that my wife is a charitable woman.'

'You have everything,' the monk said. 'So why don't you give me one rupee?'

'I have millions of rupees,' the merchant's chest puffed up. 'I have factories and shops, cars and huge mansions, any one of which could shame a palace.'

'But you do not have one rupee on you, do you?' the monk asked patiently.

The man sighed and searched in his pockets. He took out his wallet, which was stuffed with money and peered into it.

'I don't have a rupee,' he said contemptuously. 'Who keeps a rupee these days?'

'So then, you don't have everything,' the monk answered. 'You don't have a rupee.'

The man turned on his heel and walked away. His wife took back the proffered money and followed her husband. Then she suddenly turned and ran back to the monk. She stood in front of him and folded her hands.

'Please don't curse him for his rudeness,' she pleaded. 'He is actually a good man.'

The monk smiled. 'I won't curse him. I don't know how to curse people.'

The woman nodded. 'I'm curious. Why did you want only one rupee?' she asked.

'Because people have forgotten the significance of a single coin. Like your husband. He has forgotten that all wealth begins with the number one. The rest are a matter of zeros.'

The woman looked sad.

'If you take only a rupee from people, what do you do when you need to buy something?' she inquired.

'I just need enough to buy a little food,' the monk replied. 'I give away the rest to beggars and street children.'

The woman touched his feet. He caressed her head fleetingly. The husband stood a distance away, frowning. He met the monk's eyes and then turned on his heel and walked away.

The monk was happy. The fat man and his wife would soon be speaking of the old days when they were not rich, and their eyes would become dreamy and their faces soft. He soon forgot about the couple. He sat in silence, watching the endless flow of people pass; some on their way to temples, some to the bazaar, and some to find a place to eat after fasting in the morning for their pujas. Often he would nod off, warmed by the sun, and his sleep would be interrupted by the clink of coins falling into his bowl as the day moved on slowly. The monk had spent similar days in Rishikesh, sitting in the sun, watching life pass by between intervals of sleep. Pilgrims thought he was in a deep state of meditation and walked on tiptoe as they passed. Some of them would throw coins into his begging bowl, which would jolt him awake.

Asananda's favourite time was dusk, when across the river, the little town of Rishikesh would get ready to decorate itself with light. It always looked like a tiny ship docked for the night – a holy little town, teeming with temples. Some of the temples are said to be older than the Mahabharata and the Ramayana. Rishikesh was holy because it was a harbour of sins big and small, and the asylum of solace. People brought with them their secret burdens, too dirty for others to see and too shameful to be told. The gathering velocity of the wrongs they had done through the years somehow propelled them to the town seeking the solace of the Ganga. Their eyes were furtive, but their laughter was an exercise in forgetting.

Asananda was woken up from his reverie by a soft, hesitant touch. He opened his eyes to see the fat merchant squatting beside him. His face wore a slightly ashamed look. The monk smiled at him reassuringly.

'I've come to seek your forgiveness,' the merchant said in a halting voice. 'I insulted you. I thought you were after my money. Everyone is so greedy these days.'

'I do not set much value by money,' said the monk. 'I seek much more valuable currency.'

'But without money, we are nothing,' the man sounded puzzled. The monk bade him to sit down. The merchant looked hesitantly at the stone platform on which the monk sat. He spread his handkerchief and lowered himself on it carefully. Asananda suppressed a smile at the large man trying to sit on such a small pocket square; indeed, he would have to sit virtually motionless to keep his pajamas from getting dirty.

'Since you are a wise man, swamiji, do you have any useful advice for me, which I may profit by? You people know all sorts of secrets,' the man said.

'What do you value the most in life?' the monk asked him.

'Money and my wife,' the man said. 'We have no children.'

'Let me tell you about a greedy king, whose touch could turn anything into gold,' said the monk.

The merchant looked at the monk scornfully. 'King Midas? Who hasn't heard that story?'

'Not the way my master told me,' Asananda replied. 'He told us lovely stories. The Buddha told the Jataka stories, but Gyanananda had his own.'

One day, an avaricious king named Midas was given a boon by a god; anything he touched would turn to gold. He happily went around his palace, touching dishes, pillars and furniture, turning them all into a glittering yellow mass. It made him ecstatic. He soon turned his attention to trees, the flowers in his garden and the horses in his stables. Soon his entire kingdom became a vast dominion of gold. He was beside himself with delight, and he went everywhere, calculating how much he was worth. His daughter complained that there was nothing to eat in the palace since one can dine on gold plates, but not on gold.

He embraced his daughter to comfort her, but to his horror, she, too, became a gold statue. The king was overcome by sorrow, and he prayed to god in vain to bring her back to life. But his greed was so great that soon he was telling himself that it was a good thing, because the princess was now worth her weight in gold.

One day, as he was walking on his gold road, along gold trees and gold rose bushes upon which gold birds sat frozen in song, Midas passed a market. He wanted to see how prosperous his people had become, since he had turned everything into gold, and secretly hoped they would praise him. To his surprise, he discovered that they were using silver coins as black market currency.

'Why are you using an inferior metal when there is so much gold?' he asked a trader angrily.

'Everything in this country is gold and only gold,' the trader replied. 'Therefore it is of no value.'

The fat man nodded thoughtfully. 'Now I understand why everyone doesn't value the same thing equally, or sometimes, not at all. Like the red stone my wife wears around her neck, which I tell her is just a trinket, but she will not let go of it for money or love.'

'What kind of red stone?' Asananda asked curiously.

'She claims it is a precious red ruby. Actually, it's a worthless piece of stone she has had with her since she was a child. She always wears it on a string around her neck.'

His uncle and aunt had no children. One day, the uncle bought a girl from a wandering yogi he had met through an intermediary in Dehra Dun. He did not inquire too much about her, since he knew that it was not unusual for mendicants to kidnap children and sell them to childless couples; it was better to look the other way or else, soon the police would be looking at him. The first time the merchant, who was a boy then, saw the girl, she looked so lost and pretty that then and there he decided he would marry her when he grew up. She had a little red stone on a string tied around her neck, which she would keep fidgeting with. She told her foster family that it was a ruby with a powerful curse, but everyone laughed at her since they knew she was the daughter of a mountain farmer who had sold her to the yogi for five hundred rupees. She would speak of living in luxury in a beautiful mansion with her parents and cars and servants. Her adopted parents would laugh indulgently; though privately they wondered how a farmer's child had such pretty manners. Maybe she had been a servant in the mansion and picked up fancy airs watching the children of the house.

As she grew older, the stories about a woman with shining black hair and a handsome man with an Elvis Presley curl, servants, cars, boats and the house on the hill stopped as they faded from her memory. The merchant married her when she turned fifteen and he, seventeen. Even after they became rich and he could afford to buy her the most expensive gold ornaments, she insisted on wearing the red stone around her neck; though he eventually persuaded her to wear it on a gold chain.

'Ketaki is happy being with me, but I've always felt that she hankers after something she lost a long time ago,' the merchant said. 'If only I could give it to her, it would make her happiness complete.'

'You can,' said Asananda. 'You can give her the gift of memory.'

The man looked puzzled.

'Go to Rishikesh and look for a fruit-seller by the name of Amogh. And your wife will make a pomegranate tree bloom.'

The merchant gazed searchingly at the monk's face, as if looking for some hidden meaning. The monk placed his palm on the merchant's head. 'Go,' he said. 'Take your wife and complete her journey with her. Everything is a circle waiting to be completed. It all starts with zero and ends with zero. You, as a merchant, would understand it well,' Asananda joked.

He got up. He realized he had not eaten. As he got closer to the bridge over the Ganga, the large clusters of shops and teahouses thinned. A group of urchins followed him like a ragged retinue, begging for money or something to eat. The monk gave them the pickings of the day, saving one rupee for his money pouch, adding to his meagre travel money. They squealed in delight at their unexpected fortune and ran away, shrieking, waving their hands and laughing. The monk entered a small roadside teashop. He sat down on a wooden bench. The shopkeeper saluted him and brought him a glass of milky tea. A bun and some curried potato followed. The shopkeeper stood beside the monk and watched him eat. He wore a curry-stained vest and a saffron dhoti; after all, he did business in a holy city and saffron was god's colour. The monk finished eating, and took out some rupee coins. The shopkeeper refused.

'I watched you give away your money to the street children,' he told the monk. 'If I don't take your money, I get blessed twice. Once by god for feeding you, and then, by the poor on the street for looking after them. Karma is a circle and feeding you is cheap compared to the grace of god.'

The monk thanked him and left. It was getting dark, and he had some way to go before he reached Joshimath. It was around eight hundred kilometres to Kailash Mansarovar, and he had covered so little of the distance. The wind smelt of rain. He would find himself a small cave by the Ganga, or else sleep on any of the big flat stones under the bridge. Or find a large hospitable tree on the wayside under which he could take shelter for the night. It did not matter. He was a soldier of Shiva, a warrior of the road, and each day took him closer to Kailash. He had found the small god and it took him closer to his destination.

Far away, nursed by the whispers of the sacred Ganga, a pomegranate tree waited to bloom.

The Monk Becomes a Guru for a Day

After spending the night wrapped in his horsehair blanket under a wayside tree, Asananda walked through the opening day with the river for company. A kind motorcyclist gave him a ride for a few kilometres. It was dusk when he saw the lights of Srinagar town in the distance and quickened his steps.

Unlike the better-known capital of Kashmir that bore the same name, the Srinagar Asananda reached was the ancient capital of the Garhwal mountain kingdom, until the Gurkhas from Nepal destroyed it. Now it is just another ugly hill town with shops and dingy hotels lining the streets. The Alaknanda river frothed beneath the iron bridge that connected the town to the road as it plunged down to join the Ganga, its distant roar populated with the souls of those lost in the forests and the icy Himalayan slopes. The monk was tired. He hoped to find a bus that would take him as far as Nandaprayag or even Karanprayag, where he could find shelter in one of the many ashrams. The Himalayan foothills were full of ashrams and dharamsalas, where the traveller could get food and a place to rest. He went looking for the municipal bus stand. Pilgrims jostled and bumped against him. Beggars cried out for alms and cycle rickshaws darted in and out, sounding their tinny bells. A woman was arguing loudly with a man who was selling paani puri from baskets suspended from both ends of a bamboo pole firmly tied to the rear carrier of his bicycle. Taxi drivers clustered at corners, looking out for customers. At his approach, a tan cow looked up from nosing around in a pile of garbage. Asananda stopped at a small shop selling second-hand books that tourists – usually from the West – had left behind.

It would be nice to have a book to read, he thought. Sometimes, while resting under a tree, tired after walking for many miles or sitting in a crowded bus on its way uphill to some town on the way to Badrinath, reading was a welcome pleasure. The bookstore owner was an old man wearing a rough woollen jacket closed at the neck and a colourful cap. He peered at Asananda through the thick lenses of his spectacles, which were tied with a piece of string and fastened loosely around his neck. He had a gap-toothed smile.

'What would you like to read, swamiji?' he asked in a surprisingly young voice. 'I have everything from Kipling's *Kim* to Jeffrey Archer, Lonely Planet guidebooks and even some books in German and French. The young foreign backpackers who pass by sell me their second-hand books to make a little extra cash.'

Asananda browsed through the shelves and found a tattered copy of the *Autobiography of a Yogi* by Paramahansa Yogananda, one of the first Hindu monks to lecture in the West after Swami Vivekananda. He had left behind his copy at the ashram and was overjoyed to find the book. Gyanananda had given it to him, asking him to read the chapters over and over again. Asananda opened the book and read a stranger's name inscribed on the first leaf. He rifled through the pages, annotated with fading blue ink, and a dog-eared photograph fell out. It showed a young man and a woman with two children standing against the railings on a riverbank. In the distance he saw the outline of what looked like Manhattan. The boy straddled the man's shoulder while the girl sat on the woman's lap, gazing at the camera with solemn eyes. There was a troubled shadow in her glance.

'Ah, Yogananda, the white man's favourite,' the bookshop owner cackled. 'George Harrison loved it. So did Elvis. Take it. It's a good read for the way. And it's only five rupees.'

Asananda held up the photograph. The old man shrugged.

'Odd, I never noticed it,' he said. 'They look like Americans.'

'Probably,' Asananda said. 'Shall I leave it with you?'

The old man held up his hands. 'No, please, take it with you. It will make a good bookmark. It has probably served as one for years.'

Asananda turned the first few pages of the book, and saw that it was a 1970 reprint. He put the photograph back into the pages and the book in his bag, gave the man five rupees, and walked on. Soon he would find a bus and would lean back on his seat and read a bit about the yogi's travels. As he began to walk towards the bus terminal, a commotion snagged his attention.

Near the bend in the road that forked – one going towards the exit of the town and the other sloping down towards the river – a crowd had gathered. He sensed a change in the atmosphere; a subtle darkness, as if a cloud lingered over the sun. The air felt sullen. The monk could hear much jeering and laughing. A shrill voice rose above the din, 'Beat him, and beat him to death.'

Someone in the crowd picked up the chant and others followed. Asananda elbowed his way to the front. The crowd had encircled a small boy who lay curled up on the ground, his knees drawn up to his chest and his hands covering his head. The atmosphere was claustrophobic with the smell of sweat and bloodlust. Asananda saw a thin, sun-browned, half-naked sadhu in a saffron sarong screaming and kicking the little boy. Each time he lashed out with his foot, he would jump in the air with a little wriggle of his thin hips and raise his skinny, dark arms to the sky as if beseeching Shiva to hurl down bolts of lightning on his victim. His matted tresses had come loose and slapped around his head like so many pigtails. In one hand he held aloft a small brass trident that flashed in the sun. The boy's stocky little frame shook with each kick. A low keening rose from his throat.

Asananda grabbed the sadhu's hand. The force of the grip made the sadhu lose his balance. He shouted obscenities as he fell to the ground in a tangle with the boy. The trident flew out of his hand and someone in the crowd cried out sharply. Asananda turned towards the crowd. It had fallen silent. Someone started to say something and stopped on seeing the monk's face.

'What is going on? Why are you trying to kill this child?' Asananda asked furiously.

A man in the crowd suddenly laughed loudly. 'That's not a child, that's an idiot.'

The fallen sadhu scrambled up, gathering his sarong. His spat at Asananda, who sidestepped the thick blob of spit.

'The bastard tried to steal from me,' the sadhu swore. 'He pulled at my satchel. It had money in it. Who the hell are you to stop me?'

He tried to kick the fallen figure on the ground. Asananda raised his hand and the sadhu stopped. He opened his mouth to abuse, but something in the monk's face made him bite his words down.

Asananda squatted down beside the boy. The boy's face was covered in blood. One eye was closed and swollen. He was bleeding through his nose. His hair was matted with blood, tears and dust. The monk noticed the boy's head was too large for his body. His arms and legs were stunted. He was dressed in a red checked shirt one size too large and a pair of loose khaki trousers. The boy whimpered; he wriggled closer to the monk as if sensing his sympathy.

'Did you steal from this man?' Asananda pointed to the sadhu who regarded them with baleful eyes.

The boy shook his head. 'I was thaking him thu my motheh,' he lisped through swollen lips. 'She wanthed a guru.'

Asananda was puzzled.

'He dhidhn't want thu come, so I tried thaking him with me,' the boy continued. Asananda understood. He felt disgusted. Then he felt angry. He knew that as a monk he was not supposed to feel angry.

'You call this boy an idiot,' he said, looking up at the crowd, 'but all of you seem to be bigger idiots.'

A low, angry grumble ran through the crowd. Asananda grasped the small, misshapen figure's hand.

'Only idiots would hurt someone who is unfortunate,' he said. 'Why? Are you afraid of him?'

'Why should we be afraid of a simple-minded dwarf? We can throw him in the Ganga with one hand,' a voice shouted from the back of the crowd. Heads nodded and there were murmurs of agreement all around.

'That would only make you a murderer, and this one's soul will get salvation by falling in the holy waters,' Asananda said. He reached out and grasped the nearest man's hand. It belonged to a strong, tall farmer, who wore a fresh vermillion tilak on his forehead. He instinctively pulled back. Asananda smiled gently. He slowly pulled the farmer's hand towards the large head of the boy, who seemed to be unaware of what was happening. He kept swaying back and forth, speaking gibberish to himself in a monotonous undertone, occasionally pausing to wipe his bloodied face.

'Touch him, go on,' Asananda told the farmer. 'It's just another person.'

'I'm not going to touch it,' the farmer said angrily. 'It's cursed.'

'You are afraid of this boy because he is different. Because you cannot understand him, and you are afraid you would become like him. You know it's absurd, but you are afraid he will infect you.'

'Even god can't understand him,' the man spat at the monk.

'God understands everyone,' Asananda said. 'Aren't we all idiots to god?'

The farmer wrenched his hand away angrily and pushed his way out of the crowd muttering loudly that two idiots should be left together and normal people should go about their own ways. There was some mild laughter, and the crowd dispersed slowly. The affronted sadhu spat at the boy before he turned and left. Asananda stroked the boy's head.

'What's your name?' he asked.

'Raju,' he said shyly.

'What do you want from that sadhu? Where are your folks?' he asked.

'I wanth tho buy a gudhu, thooking for a gudhu ...' the little figure stuttered through torn lips. Asananda tenderly wiped the boy's face with the cloth he wore over his shoulders. The boy sat up.

'Who told you to buy a guru?' Asananda asked.

The boy raised his face and looked straight into the monk's face with his good eye. It was dark, fathomless and calm. It was like looking at the universe. He sat up, one hand still clutching the edge of Asananda's garment.

'Mummy askthed me to buy a gudhu,' the boy lisped. He showed the monk a coin he had held clutched in his palm.

'Mummy gave me dhis thu buy a gudhu,' he said.

It was a one-rupee coin.

He gave it to Asananda. 'Now you ath mine,' the boy lisped loudly, grabbing the monk's hand. 'I bouth you.'

'But I'm not a guru,' Asananda protested. The boy's face twisted and his hands clenched. He started to howl. His face was purple and black with bruises. Asananda drew him close and shushed him. 'It's all right, let's go and see your mother and tell her you have bought a guru. Where is she?'

The boy pointed ahead. A bus lumbered around the bend in the road, lurching like a wounded elephant, honking and belching. Religious songs and sermons blared from speakers kept outside music shops, which were bright with garlands of coloured lights. The monk paused at a paan shop to ask where the ashrams in Srinagar were. Usually, in holy places, they stood side by side in a specific part of the town. He did not know the name of the place where his new charge's mother was. The shopkeeper asked him to walk ahead for a while, until he reached the street of the ashrams.

Asananda walked on, holding the boy's hand. They passed the bus stand and the monk looked wistfully at the travellers waiting for transport. The sun was at its highest and the air was sultry with the promise of rain. If the incident with the boy hadn't happened, he would've been in Karanprayag by now.

'Are you hungry?' he asked his new charge. The boy nodded eagerly. They entered a small teashop and ate a meagre meal of fried bread and chickpeas. After that, they set out to find Raju's mother. They wandered around the town, looking in markets, temples and the many ashrams of Srinagar, inviting curious looks from locals and tourists.

It was getting dark. Asananda was worried that he would not be able to continue his journey until he returned the boy to his mother. A distance away, Asananda saw a long cluster of buildings burst into light along the riverbank as a loud cacophony of bells announced worship time. He recognized them as modern ashrams, part of the vast religious enterprise that dominates India's holy places, and felt sad at the thought of Gyanananda and the calm retreat he had come to see as his home. The ashrams in Srinagar were imposing structures, built on acres of well-developed land with lawns, fountains, yoga pavilions and huge, air-conditioned sermon halls presided over by gigantic thrones of gold, silver and velvet and studded with gems, from which the gurus delivered their sonorous orations on karma and moksha. Garishly painted cement statues of the Hindu pantheon guard the gates. The walls of the prayer halls and the lecture room would be lined with marble imported from Italy or quarried from Rajasthan. Their floors would be covered with rugs and mattresses, on which devotees could sit, leaning on fluffy bolsters, to listen to sermons or sing bhajans. The monk knew that the gurus of these ashrams were successful televangelists; there were so many popular religious TV channels in India. They repeated their speeches to the crowds who have heard them countless times, but still wanted more. They were mostly fat men with double chins and gigantic paunches. They wore silk robes and multiple gold chains entwined with rudraksh beads. All of them claimed to have performed miracles and studied under the masters of Gyanganj – a mysterious place in the Himalayas where immortal sages lived. As the monk and the boy passed the marble gates of a large ashram guarded by two huge, colourful terracotta kapalikas, he heard snatches of a pre-recorded speech, '... all karma is washed away by charity to the guru.'

'Rajuuu,' a woman's loud shriek sounded behind Asananda. 'Hey, you sadhu, where are you taking my boy? Are you kidnapping him? I'm going to call the police.'

Asananda turned to see a middle-aged woman rushing towards them, her arms held out, her grey hair in disarray and the grey dupatta of her salwar kameez flailing in the wind. She stopped and pulled out a cell phone from her bag threateningly. The monk raised his hands to show he meant no harm. The boy ran towards her, dragging the monk behind him. His grip was surprisingly strong. They almost collided with the woman in the middle of the sidewalk. A villager selling mint-scented water under a street lamp swore at them. When the woman saw her son's injured face, she sat down on her haunches, wailing and hugging him to her breast. The boy looked at Asananda and grinned happily through punctured lips. One tooth was broken, dripping bloody saliva.

'He told me his mother was in an ashram. I was trying to find her, but there are so many ashrams here,' the monk said. 'Did you send him to buy a guru?' he inquired.

The woman frowned at him. Her face looked blank. Then she slapped her forehead. 'What do I do with this boy? I was at the ashram, trying to get a discount on a puja for him. It's so expensive, even a simple milk ablution of Lord Shiva costs five hundred rupees. He started screaming for attention and I gave him a rupee and asked him to find a guru and leave me in peace. People were getting angry at his shouting. They always get angry with Raju for some reason,' she paused.

'They are afraid of him,' Asananda said.

The woman laughed disbelievingly. 'Afraid of Raju? He should be ashamed, wandering away like that. No doctor can cure him. I've been making the rounds of temples and ashrams for ten years. I've sold almost all the land I have in my village to spend on pujas for him to recover and be normal. I've given thousands of rupees in charity to sadhus. I've spent even more on astrologers and priests, but god's ears remain closed,' she said despairingly.

Asananda caressed the boy's head gently. 'Maybe you should stop spending money on priests. If god cannot hear you, maybe your son can hear god. Isn't that better?' he said.

The boy gripped the monk's hand tightly and looked at his mother.

'I bouth you a gudhu,' he said proudly.

The woman apologized. 'I'm sorry he has caused you so much trouble. Please don't curse him. He is a simple, loving boy, but he can't express himself well.'

'People curse themselves the most,' the monk said. 'I don't curse anyone.'

'He is my only son. After I'm dead, who will look after him? His father left me when he realized Raju is not like other children. He was angry that I bore him an idiot,' she said sadly.

'Your son will be cared for, even after you are gone. He just bought a guru, didn't he?' Asananda said.

The woman gently pried Raju's fingers away from the monk's wrist. He protested.

'Thank you,' she said through a small sob caught in her throat, a wounded moth fluttering. 'You promise me that?'

'Yes,' Asananda said simply. 'My guru protects me. He will guard whoever believes in me. That's because I'm not a guru.'

When he turned to leave, the boy didn't cry.

'Goodbye little one,' Asananda said, ruffling the boy's hair, 'for now.' The large head turned upward to face him. He regarded Asananda in stillness for a long moment. Then he smiled and the monk felt the shadows of the night become lighter.

The excitement had tired him. He realized that he had not eaten. He had to find an alms house. He didn't want to stay in the dharamsalas of big ashrams. Instead, he hoped to find a small inn where he could get some rice and dal. Asananda walked away, his heart filled with happiness for he had learned that there is innocence even in pain and that the guru's grace brings the love of strangers to the unfortunate, sometimes even just briefly. But in that brief moment, like the sudden emergence of the moon in a cloudy sky, the world is revealed in all its glory as a place one calls home, no matter where or how lost one is.

The Monk and the Murderer

The streetlamps were out and the starlight was too faint to pale the shadows gathering like a conspiracy of ghosts in the narrow lanes. His steps echoed faintly along the sleeping street, past the shuttered shops and the wooden doors to ancient courtyards lying closed. From beyond the walls, an owl hooted from a hidden garden. As he passed an unlit streetlamp, Asananda felt a sudden movement, and a shadow overtook him. An old instinct returned unbidden, one honed at the military academy and in battlefields that belonged to another time, another man. He turned on the balls of his feet, letting the attacker move past swiftly, bending backward as his hand reached out to grasp the trident that would've pierced his neck had he not moved. The sadhu who had kicked Raju drew his arm back and tried to plunge the trident into his neck but Asananda, who was stronger, gripped him by the wrist, twisting his arm. He wrestled his assailant down to the ground, pressing down forcefully on his chest with his knee, holding him down with one hand. With this other hand, he seized the trident and flung it at the wall. It clattered among stones and gravel and disappeared into a culvert. His attacker cried out in pain and rage. Asananda's temples throbbed with anger. The sadhu spat in his face, eyes glittering with venom, his lips drawn back in a snarl. Asananda suddenly felt sorry for him. He released the man and stood up, stretching out his hand. Reluctantly, the sadhu clasped it and drew himself up.

'I'm sorry I hurt you,' Asananda said apologetically. 'You shouldn't sneak up on people like that.'

The sadhu looked at Asananda, searching for sarcasm. He shook his head in mild disbelief when he saw the monk's face. 'I tried to kill you, and you're saying sorry?' the sadhu burst into a laugh. He continued to laugh, doubling up, body shaking as he wiped the tears from his cheeks. Asananda stood patiently beside him. He had picked up the trident, cleaned it with the saffron cloth slung over his shoulder. He handed it back to the sadhu, who took it hesitantly, a sly wonder growing in his eyes.

'I wanted to kill you,' he said, his voice harsh and low. 'And I still want to. I think you know that. Why are you such a fool?'

Asananda smiled sadly.

'You and so many like you wear the clothes and colours of the renunciate, grow beards, let your hair grow long and matted and smear ash on your foreheads. Many even call you gurus. Yet you know so little.'

The sadhu sniggered, dusted and smoothed his clothes, and gripped his trident. 'Then bigger fools they are. But that idiot boy got what he deserved and you are a bigger idiot to interfere. What did you do with him? Sell him?'

'I returned him to his mother, but that doesn't concern you.'

'Obviously nobody would want to buy an idiot, even the desperate ones.'

'What do you mean?'

'You are too naïve to be a monk,' the sadhu grinned and spat on the ground. He looked at Asananda up and down, as if getting the measure of him. He seemed satisfied with what he saw.

'I've been looking for an assistant,' he said. 'Why don't you join me? You are tall and strong, and in case there is any trouble, I can depend on you to handle things. The pickings are good and worth the trouble.'

'What pickings?' Asananda asked.

'There are so many childless couples who would do anything to get a child. The government has made adoption laws so strict that it is easier to buy a son or daughter. And who can gain the confidence of gullible parents and children better than a sadhu?'

A deep anger welled up within Asananda.

'Are you saying you are a kidnapper?' he asked, threateningly taking a step forward to confront his attacker. The sadhu held up his hands, but his smile was sardonic and his eyes gleamed with malice.

'I didn't say that, monk, but there are enough fake sadhus willing to make a quick buck by selling a child,' he laughed.

Asananda turned away in disgust.

'You are truly evil. Don't you feel guilty?' he asked. 'Have you *ever* felt guilty?'

The sadhu looked taken aback for a moment. Then he grinned, showing betel-yellowed teeth.

'Once, only once,' he said. 'But guilt doesn't last long for the resolute and determined.'

Asananda felt unclean just listening to the sadhu. Fearing that if he heard any more, he would strike him and violate his vow as a monk, he turned and walked away. As he walked, looking for a place to stay the night, the picture of Raju's trusting face rose in his mind. The memory of walking through the streets of Srinagar, holding the boy by his hand earlier in the day, came back to him. By some sleight of starlight and memory, for a moment, the child's face was replaced with Gyanananda's. The eyes twinkled with mischief. Asananda felt his guru's familiar grip around his fingers. He felt disoriented, and the shadows seemed to gather protectively around him as he walked on in a daze.

'Master, is it you walking with me?' Asananda whispered to the night.

'I'm always walking with you, Asananda,' Gyanananda replied.

The monk felt he was travelling through a dream that was already being seen by someone else. Someone, who had charted his every step, was responsible for these random meetings with wayfarers who had many questions. Cutting through his dreamy state, he heard someone calling him from behind, shouting for him to wait. Asananda stopped. He looked back. It was the sadhu who had tried to ambush him previously. Panting, he approached Asananda, and fell at his feet and grabbed him by the ankles. His clothes were dishevelled. His hair was undone. He had lost his trident.

'Forgive me, my Lord,' he whispered, his voice trembling with fear. 'I did a great wrong trying to attack you. Please don't curse me. Please don't destroy me.'

Asananda was puzzled. He bent down and tried to free his feet from the sadhu's hold. The man shook his head, and clung to Asananda's legs, slobbering and asking for forgiveness.

'But you did nothing wrong,' Asananda said gently. 'You were only acting according to your nature.'

The sadhu looked up at the monk. Seeing the softness on his face, he got up and stood before Asananda, hands folded.

'I was chasing you to stab you with my trident again,' he said. 'But no matter how fast I ran, I just couldn't get near you. And you were walking so slowly. Only a god can do that.'

Asananda looked puzzled. The story of the robber who chased the Buddha in the forest came to him. One day, a robber met the Buddha walking in the forest and ran after him to kill him and chop off his fingers. But he couldn't catch up, however fast he ran. Hearing the robber's calls, the Buddha stopped and turned. He came up to the Bodhisattva, panting. He saw the infinite mercy on the Budha's face. He dropped the knife and his knees trembled. He asked the Bodhisattva why he couldn't catch up with one walking so slowly. The Buddha replied, 'I stopped when you called, my son, but it was you who continued to run.'

Asananda understood. He held the sadhu's shoulders and looked into his eyes. He saw swirls of an old darkness, and along with it, something new, like a water droplet shining in the dawn.

'I'm not a god, just an ordinary monk in search of the Book of Shiva,' he said. 'I was walking normally, but my guru was walking with me. You were chasing the guru, and he stopped when he heard you call.'

The shaken sadhu sat down on a stone bench by the road. Asananda sat beside him and gently placed a hand on his shoulder. The sadhu began to weep. His body shook with sobs, and as the grief and regret built up, he began to cry louder, beating his bony chest. 'I'm sorry I kicked and beat that child and then tried to kill you. Will you forgive me?' he wailed.

'I've nothing to forgive you for,' he said. 'And Raju bears nobody any ill will.'

'I've done many bad things in my life, terrible things,' the sadhu sobbed. 'My real name is Puran and I come from a village of boatmakers by the Ganga. In my youth, I was a river rider. I wanted a girl badly, but she preferred someone else. I killed her and escaped in a silver boat her lover had made. I reached

Rishikesh and sold the boat to a young boatman and fled, because it was a matter of time before the police came looking for me.'

Asananda closed his eyes tight and felt the tears trembling behind his lids. He thought of the man Roopvati's father had murdered, mistaking him for her lover. He thought of Roopvati's agony, her endless search for her song and all the years she lost in pain and heart-rending hope.

It is the fate of the seeker to learn lessons from the sorrows of others, when it becomes his own, the monk thought. No lesson is learnt without experiencing the summer of suffering, and fortunate are the ones who learn it in the shade of the guru's grace.

To the sadhu, he did not know what to say.

'After the murder, to escape the police, I disguised myself as a sadhu and lived in ashrams in Rishikesh. I had no money, and I stole whenever I could. One day, I was passing a huge mansion on a hill and saw a little girl playing with a stone. She was a very pretty girl. I gave her a toffee, which was laced with hashish. She quickly fell asleep. I grabbed her and ran away. Later, I sold her. After that, I kidnapped many children and sold them too.'

Asananda felt sickened in the face of such evil and turned away.

'Wait, I want to tell you everything. Remember, you asked me earlier whether I ever felt guilty and I said once?' Asananda felt he did not have the strength to hear any more and feared that the knowledge of the sadhu's transgressions would settle in his heart like a foul burden he would carry forever. Sensing his reluctance the sadhu gripped the monk's hand. Asananda fliched.

'There is one deed of mine that still haunts me. One day, when I was begging for food, a woman gave me some coins. Her son was leaving for school, bathed, groomed and all dressed up in his neatly pressed uniform. When I saw him, I thought, what a good price the boy would fetch me. The mother even made him touch my feet. Later, I followed him, and on a lonely stretch, dragged him into the bushes. My plan was to drug him and take him away to sell. Before I could do that, we heard the sound of a car approaching and the boy began to struggle and scream for help. I was frightened. I clamped my hand down on his mouth to stop his shouting. He kept struggling and I tightened my grip. He stopped moving after a while, but I didn't remove my hand. By the time the car passed, and I finished waiting to see if any more vehicles were coming, he was dead. I waited for night to come and took his body and threw it in the Ganga. Sometimes, I still feel his hot breath on my palms.'

Asananda remembered the woman who had accosted him on the road from Shivpuri, looking for her bastard son. He remembered her agonized face, the trembling frame and desperate voice. He remembered seeing her at peace at last, on the bier in the charnel house; he remembered lighting her pyre.

Suddenly, he wanted retribution to rain down on the sadhu, and the fires of Shiva's wrath to turn him into ash. He closed his eyes hoping it was a nightmare, and wanted the sadhu to disappear. The words of the Bodhisattva filled his ears, spoken in Gyanananda's voice. It urged him to understand that even the most fallen human being deserved salvation. His heart rebelled against it. He felt the bile rise to his throat. He wanted to kill the sadhu, take his neck in his strong hands, and wring it. But the guru's insistent voice slowly filled his mind like a spring, trying to calm him down. Asananda remembered the story of the Buddha and the robber again. 'Have you heard of the story of Angulimala, the robber who chased the Buddha and couldn't catch up with him?' he asked. He suddenly felt detached. His voice was in the grip of a distant ventriloquist, his words were not his own.

'Like I couldn't catch you?' asked the sadhu.

'Listen to me, sadhu,' said the monk. 'Like you, Angulimala, too, had done terrible things. But after he met the Buddha, he renounced his evil ways and became a monk and was saved.'

'I doubt I will ever be saved,' said the sadhu. 'There is no Buddha to save a criminal like me.'

'Everyone can be saved by the guru. When Angulimala became a monk of the Buddha, he was reborn, and thereby became pure,' answered Asananda in Gyanananda's words.

'I am lost forever,' the sadhu said. 'While halting at many ashrams as I travelled looking for a child to steal or a pilgrim to rob, I have heard many sermons. The Atharva Veda describes a place in hell, a realm of endless night where murderers live in despair and pain. They are tortured to death over and over again. That is my fate.'

Asananda got up. He found it difficult to truly forgive the sadhu.

'I have to go now, for I have to go far,' he said. 'Seek the grace of the guru, and he may save your soul after all.'

'What if I don't have one?' the sadhu asked, his voice shivering in terror. 'What if I have already given to it to the demons who await me in hell?'

Asananda did not have an answer. He muttered a hasty blessing in a hurry to leave. As he walked away into the night, the sadhu's sobs followed him like a crowd of desperate, frightened ghosts.

Asananda realized that regret had already claimed the sadhu, and soon, remorse, its terrible cousin, would throw its great dark cloak over him.

Asananda remembered his guru telling him that remorse is the master of responsibility, and an exacting one. Feeling its whiplashes are the inevitable first steps towards salvation. Those who feel the torment start to flee, first from the past that has become their hunter, and then from themselves, because they are consumed by it. The road to salvation is full of thorns that tear their skin away, rocks that cut and cripple their feet, and great crevices into which they would fall to demons that wait in the darkness, accomplished in the exquisite tortures of despair. They will cry out into the empty sky, to be freed of the agony that has become greater than that of the pain they have caused others. They are destined to suffer it over and over again. It is called hell. Everyone makes their hell, god doesn't have to do a thing about it.

Asananda felt grateful that Gyanananda had cast his mantle of mercy and protected him as he walked through a varied landscape in which the pain of his fellow men had left behind barren gardens. It was his destiny to plant little acorns of his guru's grace, in the hope that they would grow into great trees and cast benign shade for souls that seek shelter from the wrath of karma's fiery star.

The monk walked along the yellow lamp-lit road, stepping on shadows. The flow of the river kept him company. A nighthawk cried. The monk looked around. The street was empty, stretching like a loose, winding cloth made of shadows and light. He thought about the wasted lives of so many children, the ravaging of innocence and wondered about a divinity that allowed such things to happen. His guru had told him about the implacable circle of karma that everyone was subject to, and had witnessed it in Roopvati and Amogh. But he couldn't comprehend the evil in the heart of man and how it ate at the soul. Lost in his reverie, he was interrupted by the sound of a gate opening. He stopped. He was in front of an old building. Beyond the walls, he could see the shadowy forms of trees, and the soft notes of a hymn reached him like an invitation. A small boy dressed in a white loincloth stood at the gate.

'Come inside,' he said in a low, modulated voice. 'The master asked us to expect you.'

The monk wondered where he was.

'At the ashram of the Order of Hope in Srinagar,' the boy replied as he led Asananda inside. 'Tonight, you eat and rest. Tomorrow morning, you can take the bus to Nandaprayag.'

Asananda felt light and free, as if he was treading on the wind. The sadhu seemed like a bad dream, and he gave thanks to his guru for giving him shelter on his path, free from the malevolence of man. His heart exulted at the thought that each day brought him closer to the Himalayas and the Book of Shiva.

The Monk and the Lost Path
of the Buddha

The stars still powdered the sky when the monk boarded the bus to Nandaprayag. The Ganga thundered below as the ramshackle vehicle groaned uphill. The road climbed higher towards Joshimath, about a hundred kilometres away. The sun was making for its place in the centre of a sparse blue sky. The air became sharper and cleaner. It smelt of rhododendrons and river water. The sunlight held a sharp coolness. The mountains sloped away on either side in green and ochre furrows, clothed in underbrush and blooming shrubbery. Clusters of pine trees, oak and cypresses leaned towards the travelling water. Their shadows fell ahead on the mossy rocks below, long and dark. The road twisted and turned, revealing different vistas. Thin footpaths resembling lines on a gigantic palm picked their way down through slate-coloured rocks. Green terraced fields quilted the valley below. The mountainsides were sheared in places, revealing swathes of brown earth. The rains had washed away parts of the slopes. Through the window of the bus, the monk saw occasional clusters of houses on faraway hilltops that stood like outposts of some forgotten civilization. The sun glittered on the distant snow on the great Himalayan crests. The bus passed small shops that sold colourful plastic buckets and mugs, with gunnysacks full of rice and potatoes covered with tarpaulin sheets. Sturdy mountain men with leathery faces smoked stoically on benches outside. They waved at the monk. He smiled at them. Further on, a small boy in ragged but clean clothes was watching over goats grazing on the slope. The boy raised his stick and shouted at a bleating kid that was venturing down a gulch. A convoy of Tata Safari SUVs, loaded with skis and snow equipment, roared by, dissipating diesel smoke. They were bound for Auli, ahead of Joshimath.

The bus passed the bustle of Karanprayag, with the ubiquitous cluster of ramshackle buildings that hugged the sides of every hill town. Asananda was thirsty and hungry. He could do with a piece of bread and some water. Even some hot tea would be good. As if god heard him, the bus stopped at a small teashop that stood under an oak tree at the junction of a mountain path and the highway. It had a frontage of bricks held together with clay. Under a low roof, its interior was dark. A pile of laddoos, covered with thin gauze to keep flies away, stood on a shelf. A couple of tins holding biscuits and rusks kept it company along with a loaf of bread. The passengers, who had alighted and clustered around the shop, bought snacks and lemonade. The owner of the teashop offered the monk a glass of steaming hot tea. He thanked the man who wore a dirty burlap cap. He was rewarded with a gap-toothed smile. The monk held the hot glass close to his chest for warmth. He was about to take a sip when he saw two Buddhist monks turn the curve of the mountain path. To his surprise, he noticed that one of them was walking backwards as his companion loped alongside, warning him of obstructions. They stopped at the teashop.

'Today seems to be a bad day for business,' joked the teashop owner. 'With only monks as customers, it seems I won't be making much money.'

Asananda took out some coins from his pouch, which the teashop owner refused. 'I don't want to spoil my afterlife,' he said. 'Feeding monks will add to my good karma.'

'In which case, maybe you could give me a bun and a banana, too but I'm paying. If I eat free, I will be indebted to you. So both of us will have to be reborn again to meet our debts,' Asananda said, placing some rupees on the rough wooden table, stained with rings of tea glasses. The teashop owner, perturbed at the thought of repaying karmic debts, hastily picked up the money.

The Buddhist monks came and sat down beside Asananda. One was old and the other barely twenty. Their heads were shaved in the tradition of Buddhist bhikshus. Both wore ochre civaras – most Buddhist monks were expected to wear three robes: an inner robe worn around the waist to reach below the knee, an upper robe that covered the shoulders, and an outer overcloth. The older bhikshu walked backwards. The younger monk guided him to the bench and seated him. The sun was nearly at the centre of the sky's forehead. The teashop owner placed plates of wheat bread stuffed with spicy potatoes, two saucers of yoghurt, glasses and an aluminium kettle full of tea. The aroma of the tea swirled up along with the slim curls of steam rising through its spout.

'We have to eat before noon,' the younger bhikshu explained to Asananda as he ate the bread. 'It is the Buddhist rule for monks.'

Asananda nodded.

'I am Tapussa and he is Vallika,' the young bhikshu informed him.

'Aren't those the names of the first two disciples of the Buddha?' asked Asananda. Tapussa seemed pleased. Vallika looked up from his plate at Asananda keenly.

'Where are you bound?' Asananda asked.

'We seek the Lost Path of the Buddha. We are from a small monastery near Rumtek. Our master has ordered us to go to ancient Muktinath, which we call Chumig Gyatsa, or the Hundred Waters. Here, Buddhists worship Lord Vishnu as Avalokitesvara, the compassionate Buddha. The Ganga flows downstream from there as Gandaki, and on the river bed there are many sacred saligram stones.'

'What is the Lost Path of the Buddha? How will you find it?'

The bhikshu answered, 'Our master had a vision. After the Buddha wandered in the wilderness, inflicting pain and suffering on himself, he reached the shores of Gandaki, beside which he was to die many years later. Our master saw him pick sacred saligram stones from the riverbed. The stones have the power to free anyone from the bane of karma. At each significant turn in his life – where Sujata offered him food, where he battled the demon Mara, where he met the robber Angulimala, where he picked up the lame lamb and calmed Devadutta's raging elephant, to where he fell sick after partaking of Chunda's food and, in the end, where he initiated Subhadda, his last monk – the Buddha buried one saligram each. We seek those hidden stones. It is the map to salvation.'

Asananda closed his eyes and meditated on the Ganga that runs through the lives of all prophets, receiving them in the end as the children of wisdom and knowledge.

'A wise man walks along many roads, but he walks only one path,' said Tapussa. 'Just as one journeys on a river, but stops at a few wharves, a true path is hidden within every journey, which is its soul. We seek the one that the Buddha walked.'

'Where will you find the sacred stones?' Asananda asked.

'They are hidden at forks on the secret road,' the bhikshu replied. 'The saligrams show the true seeker the right path. After all, at strange crossroads, how do we know which direction to go? Do we take the path of destiny or the path of grace?'

'How will you tell them apart?'

'By perceiving the past and the present at the same time,' Tapussa interrupted. 'That is why I walk backwards while my friend here walks ahead. The past is your destiny, and you cannot change it. The future is a state of grace, which you seek as you move towards god.'

'I'm looking for the Book of Shiva and you are seeking the Lost Path of the Buddha,' said Asananda wryly. 'What a merry dance our masters have led us on.'

'Our master told us a Jataka story about two merchants,' said Tapussa. 'It may, perhaps, explain why we are on our respective journeys. Would you like to hear it?'

'Provided we have enough time,' Asananda said, raising his chin towards the bus. The passengers were getting ready to continue their journey. The driver threw away his unfiltered cigarette and clambered on to his seat.

The Monk Gets Two Companions

The bus driver leaned on the horn, signalling loudly to the passengers that it was time to continue their journey. Suddenly, Asananda did not feel like getting up. He wanted to sit with the bhikshus. He was curious about the Lost Path of the Buddha. He asked for more tea. The bus conductor called out to the monk, but Asananda smiled and waved, indicating the bus should proceed without him. The man shrugged, and gave a piercing whistle. With a groan, the bus lurched forward, leaving a train of black diesel smoke. Asananda offered the bhikshus tea. They raised their palms, saying it was past noon and they could not accept food according to their custom.

'We are taught that our journey through time and through many lives leads us to liberation,' Tapussa spoke. 'Each life has a lesson, and the many lives of the Buddha hold many lessons, which form the Jataka fables. The story I'm about to tell holds a helpful moral.'

In one of his previous lives, the Buddha reached a village dressed as a mendicant. He met two merchants who were friends and competitors. The harvests were good and the merchants were getting ready to travel to the nearest town to sell their produce. It was a long and tedious journey. The Buddha asked for a ride on any of their carts. The first merchant was a greedy person. 'You will add to the weight of my caravan if I give you a seat on one of my carts,' he said. 'I will only be able to carry less to the market, and therefore my profits will be smaller.'

He said that he would go first to study the market so that the traders there would not cheat the second merchant when he arrived. Secretly, he calculated that if he went first, the road would be better, and not rutted by other carts, and thereby would ensure a comfortable journey. There would be enough vegetation on the wayside for his bullocks to eat, since he would be travelling on that road before anyone else. The trees would be ripe with fruits to pluck and he could also bargain with the farmers for vegetables that grew in the fields by the road. The second merchant agreed for he was a kind man. As the greedy merchant set off, the Buddha warned him, 'On your way, you will reach a fork in the road. One will take you through the Waterless Desert. It is full of demons that prey on travellers. Be careful and take enough water with you. The second fork will put you on the Road of Floods, with huge cracks where the road has caved in. You will meet men with rafts who promise to take you across. But they are demons that will devour you once you drown. So do not take it.'

'So which one do I choose?' the merchant asked sarcastically. 'According to you, both will lead me to my destruction.'

'Maybe I know another way, if only you would take me with you,' said the Buddha.

The merchant roared with laughter, slapping his thighs in merriment.

'What sort of a fool do you think I am to fall for a trick like that? The Waterless Desert and the Road of Floods are myths.'

He whipped his bullock, which grunted and started off, followed by the rest of the caravan. At the crossroads, he took the path that passed the Waterless Desert. On the way, he was met by demons disguised as villagers, carrying water pitchers, fresh fruits and flowers. 'Why do you carry all that food and water? There are so many villages ahead, where you can get plenty of both. Throw away all your jars, pots and pans. Allow us to travel with you for a short distance until we reach our village, and we will fill your carts with enough produce, which you can sell when you reach the town.'

Overjoyed, the greedy merchant took the demons' advice. As they travelled on, they reached a desert. The caravan trudged on, and the animals were exhausted without food and water. The thirsty merchant kept asking his new passengers where the promised food and water was. Just a little ahead, the demons would promise. Finally, the caravan collapsed with hunger and thirst. As they lay defenceless and weak, they were set upon by the evil ones and devoured, leaving only chalky skulls and bones behind.

After a few weeks, the second merchant started his journey. He knew the caravan preceding him would have levelled the roads for his carts to travel, and he wouldn't have to get off and push if any got stuck in the ruts. The first merchant's animals would have eaten up all the old grass, leaving tender shoots to grow for the ones who followed. The first merchant would only get old fruits and vegetables, leaving the second fresh ones to buy. The Buddha asked the second merchant if he could come along. He thought for a while. 'One of my drivers has fallen ill. If you can drive his cart, you can travel with me.'

'Are you sure? If you drive it yourself, you can carry more and make more money,' said the Buddha.

The second merchant shook his head. Something in the mendicant's face told him it would be a wise thing to take him along. They set out, with the Buddha driving the lead cart. When they reached the fork in the road, he asked the Buddha which road was best. The Buddha smiled. He urged the caravan on through the middle of the fork, creating his own road as they went ahead.

'What is the moral of the story?' Tapussa asked Asananda.

'Take the Middle Path as the Buddha advised after his enlightenment?' asked Asananda.

'That, too,' replied Tapussa. 'Or, even better, allow god to create the middle path for you.'

'Why would god do that?'

'Because he wants to reach the other side safely, too. Or else, he would've perished as well. Without man, god cannot fulfil his own destiny.'

The shepherd boy came into sight, followed by his goats. He was holding the kid in his arms. It was bleating in pain. The teashop owner came out and stared at them.

'What a useless son you are,' he scolded the boy. 'Is that little thing hurt?'

The boy stopped by the shop, followed by the goats whose heads and necks bobbed as they walked. 'It's limping badly,' he told his father. 'It fell and got trapped between some rocks. I had to climb down to get it.' He rubbed his bruised shins.

'You deserve it for being so careless about your animals. What will we do with a lame goat? We'll have to sell it to the butcher,' the teashop owner shouted again.

Tapussa held his arms out. The boy gave him the kid. The animal bleated, its hurt leg kept folded below its neck. The elderly bhikshu covered it with his upper cloth, and passed his hands over its injured part. After a few moments, the kid bleated and hopped down from the monk's lap.

'A miracle!' said the teashop owner, falling to the ground, his forehead touching the bare earth. The boy looked back and forth at his father and the monks, his mouth open. The kid bleated merrily and went hopping away, searching for food.

'I see that you have found one of your saligrams, a healed goat,' Asananda remarked half in jest, getting up from the bench and picking up his satchel and staff. 'I have to be going.'

'Saligrams are also objects of power, made by Vishnu,' Tapussa said. 'They unlock the secrets that await the true seeker.'

'How do they do it?'

'When you become Buddha, you will know it.'

'But I thought you were the ones collecting the saligrams,' Asananda protested. 'And how do I become Buddha? Is it the same as becoming Shiva?'

'Anyone can become Buddha,' Tapussa said. 'Or Shiva for that matter, I'm sure. Once you have done all you have done, and know that nothing more needs to be done to become nothing, at last, you become Buddha.'

'The Buddha lives in all, only most of us don't know it,' said Vallika. 'We throw away the gifts given to us by our ancestors, the gods and fate. In the end, we don't even know why we are sad without realizing that we had the power to make ourselves happy.'

The bhikshus got up.

'Can I walk with you for a while?' asked Asananda.

Asananda looked at the two, one facing him and the other looking backwards.

'Come,' Tapussa said. 'Being on the Lost Path of the Buddha with you is a privilege.'

As they started off, Tapussa's feet faltered on a stone. Vallika gripped his arm to stop him from falling. The elder bhikshu muttered something in a decidedly un-Buddhist manner. Asananda laughed. 'Perhaps you should stick to the middle path,' he observed. Tapussa laughed aloud.

'On the path that my master put me on, I've discovered some saligrams of my own,' Asananda told them. 'I've discovered that to succeed on any journey, it needs a master's blessing. I've learned about the power of true hope in a garden of pomegranates, which teaches one the art of waiting. I've learned that along a journey will be found a silver boat to take you across and leave you on the shore of learning. I found that there are those who are destined to wait for you and only you, because each one has been given an angel of salvation, which cannot happen without a guru's grace. I've realized that families start preparing you for that journey when you are but a child and the lessons of our elders are endowed with miracles as enchanting as magical swallows. I've learned of the small god, who is none but Lord Shiva himself. I've learned of the tragedy of greed, whose comedy of coincidences leads to sadness. I've learned that wisdom lies in innocence, even if one is not aware of possessing either. I've discovered that one meets companions on one's path, who teach you how to discover yourself and the universe, either through meanness, love or simply by travelling together. If my master hadn't sent me to find the Book of Shiva, I would not have learned all this.'

'You are on your way to becoming Buddha,' said Vallika laughingly.

'My master said I will one day become Shiva,' said Asananda. 'Maybe it is the same thing.'

The shadow of a cloud passed over them like the canopy of a blessed tree as the monks moved towards the Himalayas in comfortable silence.

The Monk Finds Hospitality by the River

When the travellers reached Nandaprayag, night had fallen. The little town dozed to the chant of the Nandakini river, which embraced the Alaknanda on its perennial way down to meet its sister, Bhagirathi.

'My journey is like the meeting of many rivers that collect the detritus of things left behind, which they carry along to the ocean as one huge flow. Only, mine flows uphill, tantalizing me with mysteries on the way,' Asananda thought. As he walked up the tangled road, accompanied by his two strange companions, Asananda realized that along the Ganga, the past lay ahead, to be discovered by the future. The shadows of the two monks, one walking forward and the other backwards looked like a bizarre beast. Everything seemed to be a mirage; a life inverted by the mischief of his master. As he walked on, he knew that he would encounter little villages that clung obstinately for decades, perhaps centuries, to steep mountain slopes above the roaring, frothing river. He would smell the spicy scent of pine forests in the air that got thinner as he climbed higher. He would stop to pay obeisance at shrines big and small. He would wonder about the ageless caves at the foot of mountains and imagine the innumerable ascetics who have sought to open the hidden third eye on their forehead to witness the glory of Lord Shiva. There would be monasteries on the way that have calmly witnessed, from great mountain heights, the passage of centuries. At the end of his journey waited the sacred Himalayas that were born from the primeval ocean after the gods and demons churned the sea in search of the urn of immortality. Somewhere in those gigantic heights, hidden by snow and curtained by fierce winds, lay a cave, which was part of his past. Now, it was going to be his future again, where he hoped to find the Book of Shiva. At least that was the impression his master gave him, if he had understood Gyanananda correctly.

But then masters are mysteries unto themselves, the monk thought. They spend their lives unravelling the mystery that each person is. In their unravelling, their disciples learn the secrets of the gods.

As if he had sensed the monk's thoughts, Tapussa asked, 'Has it ever occurred to you that meeting the Buddha is the purpose of life? The master sends you on a journey of transformation, changing you and everything around you. A disciple's deepest desire is to be like his master, but the master wants more. He wants the disciple to be him. And at the end of that journey, you and the master become one. Thus, you become the Buddha.'

By changing me, Gyanananda changed my journey, Asananda thought.

Far away, he heard the Ganga's roar, the great cry of the northern wind spreading through untravelled forests. He heard it all, the sudden sigh of a falling star as it entered the earth's atmosphere, the gentle heaving of rock under the great mountains, the eternal breathing of the oceans, the great subterranean creaking of the continents and the hiss of magma.

I cannot see it, but I know it's all there. It's real. Just like the master's grace. It is the invisible skin of the universal drum, which the world strikes to make its music, sometimes beautiful, sometimes discordant.

'The sound of one-hand clapping' – the phrase came to him unbidden and unexpected.

The breath of the travellers formed shapes in the cold air. Strangely, Asananda did not feel cold. His body seemed to have summoned old memories of its own: of sadhus and Brahma bulls, the thunder clap of mortar fire in the mountains, days and nights spent in a distant cave outside which blizzards raged, thundering with the screaming of the spirits that roamed the endless snows. The warmth of the leopard skin, which he had once sat upon and meditated, seemed to envelop him. It rose through his limbs, kindling his blood, quickening the beat of his heart. The night sky was clear, a deep cobalt blue. The stars shone, bright and hard. The air was getting thinner and sharper. The wind soughed in the forests.

'We should look for a place to sleep,' said Tapussa. 'There must be an inn for pilgrims or a monastery somewhere here.'

'I doubt we'll find any dharamsalas welcoming pilgrims at this time. Look, the whole place is deserted and I don't expect anyone to be awake at this hour,' Vallika said. 'Perhaps we can sleep on the steps of some building. Maybe we will find some ruined house one can stay for the night, though I'm afraid of bats.'

'Maybe you wouldn't need to meet any bats,' Asananda said, pointing ahead. Some distance away, a light shone softly in the night. Its reflection was scattered on the flowing darkness of the river – a latticework of light on water that shivered as the wind skimmed the river's surface. As they walked on, a small footpath veered away from the main road and led down to the Nandakini.

The travellers could distinguish the outlines of a large building by the riverside, pencilled by nightlight.

'Aren't we lucky,' Vallika exclaimed. 'A dharamsala! We can find a warm room and mattresses. There may even be leftovers for dinner.'

Asananda laughed. Tapussa looked at his friend askance. 'We have taken the vow of austerity,' he said. 'Monks are not supposed to think of comfort.'

'Why not?' retorted Vallika. 'When the Buddha went to the forest after renouncing everything, he discovered that salvation cannot be attained by punishing the body. I see no reason why we should ignore his holy advice.'

Tapussa broke into laughter.

'This way you, too, will become the Buddha, unless the bedbugs in the mattress keep you from sleeping,' he said.

The dharamsala was a two-storied building, which was built on a rock jutting out above the river. Steps cut into a large broad rock, on which the inn stood, marched up to a huge doorway. More steps led down to a bathing enclosure protected by iron railings. Even in the faint starlight, the inn's façade was impressive. The arched gateway was shaped like a peacock fan at the top, the fanlight inlaid with coloured glass. Two slim colonettes painted with patterns of climbing vines supported the curved cornice. The entrance was framed with blue plaster. Oriel windows with trellised sides and pilasters at the sides looked down from the upper floors. The gigantic wooden door was banded and studded with iron. A small peep-window was set at a person's height on the door. Asananda knocked loudly and waited. He heard steps, and the window slid aside. It spilled light on the faces of the monks.

'We are sadhus seeking shelter,' Asananda said. 'There are three of us, but we can sleep on the veranda if there is no room available. Could you please let us in?'

The lamp was removed and a pair of dark eyes stared at them through the rectangular brightness of the window. There was a pause and the sound of a heavy wooden slider being pulled aside, followed by the dull clunking of a chain being drawn through old, iron rings. A figure wrapped in a shawl, holding a lantern, stood inside. A thin gold bangle shone on a slim wrist.

'Come in and I will prepare a room for you,' the voice was soft, but did not seem to belong to an educated person. 'Have you eaten?'

'Om namoh Narayana! Food and shelter would be welcome, thank you.' Asananda said as he stepped into the courtyard of a large peristyle, with rooms on all four sides. The woman looked at Tapussa walking backward, but made no comment. Perhaps she has seen stranger things on this pilgrims' route. She dragged the large door shut behind them and slid the log bolt into place. The monks followed her into the house.

They deposited their meagre belongings on the veranda and went down to wash in the river. When they came back, the woman served them rotis and dal. Afterwards, they were given a room that overlooked the Nandakini.

The Buddhist monks lay down on their mattresses and were instantly asleep. Asananda did not feel sleepy. The clean smell of the river in the air had dispelled his fatigue. He looked out at the huge twin rock faces plunging down into the frothing water. They resembled buried foreheads of dying elephants. Faraway, the snow waited with eternal patience.

He remembered a story his grandmother had told him about how the Himalayas were born. Aeons ago, the gods and demons were constantly at war and the demons were winning. In despair, the gods approached Lord Vishnu who asked them to find amrit – the elixir of immortality that lay hidden in the ocean bed, so that they could drink it and would not be killed. The demons protested that it was unfair that the gods were being favoured. Vishnu gave them the great serpent Vasuki, which encircled Mount Meru – the axis of the earth – in its coils to act as a churning stone. The warring parties churned the ocean for many years. In the force of the ferment, Vasuki spat out his venom, which Lord Shiva drank. It turned his throat blue. Finally, the urn holding the elixir appeared and the gods and demons fought over it. The gods managed to appropriate the elixir and therefore became immortal. In the force of the churning, the Himalayas rose up from the ocean bed, and the sea, displaced by the great mountain ranges, covered the world in a great flood that lasted many yugas.

'The Himalayas hold the secret to immortality,' Asananda remembered his master's words.

'But why would anyone wish to be immortal?' Asananda had asked. 'To gather more karma, and then be reborn to repeat the cycle all over again? How long will a soul carry the burdens of so many lifetimes?'

'Until it receives the grace of a guru,' Gyanananda had replied calmly. 'The purpose of life is finding a guru. Like Arjuna found Krishna. Or Peter found Jesus. Until then, a life is just the sound of one hand clapping.'

Asananda was startled hearing Gyanananda use the phrase. It disturbed him. They were walking through the remains of the day. They strolled along the darkening Ganga. The fortissimo of prayers and temple bells rose in the evening wind. The monk shut his eyes briefly, imagining a scene that had become so familiar through the years: monks young and old, women and children sitting in rows in ashram courtyards, clapping and swaying to the melodious Vedic rhythms that invited the grace of gods who lived on the great Himalayan peaks afar.

'Come, I'll show you something,' Gyanananda told his disciple.

'Where are we going?' Asananda asked his master.

'To where the answer to old riddles lies.'

The monk looked at his master. On his forehead, a vertical crimson sign was drawn in the centre of a thick smear of sandal paste. It seemed like an all-seeing third eye.

'I'm going to show you the sound of one hand clapping,' said the master. 'The one you always wanted to hear since you were a child.'

The monk closed his eyes and remembered the riddle of his childhood. One that belonged to another; a past that didn't seem to be his own. He nodded. The master quickened his steps. They left the brightly lit streets, passing houses that slumbered in shadow. Mendicants slept on cool, dark verandas. They passed the last of the ashrams and walked uphill. The master stopped at the foot of a gigantic banyan tree. Its knotted trunk was riddled with age and shadows. Its ancient roots hung like the matted tresses of a yogi. Steps led to a large, circular brick platform built around it. On the platform, hidden away from the road, was a small temple the height of a sitting man. Someone had lit a lamp inside it. It shone on the black dome of a shivling. It looked old. Very old. The air smelt of incense. A large shining bell, too large for the temple, hung at the door, suspended from a wooden beam. The master sat down and patted the ground beside him. Asananda lowered himself on the platform and crossed his legs.

'I have brought you to the place where all riddles are solved,' the guru said.

'What is this place?'

'Legend says this is the tree under which Lord Shiva meditated on the sound of "Om" and the silence of the universe.'

'Then show me the answer, master,' the monk said. 'Show me the sound of one hand clapping.'

The master leaned over and struck the bell with the flat of his palm. The bell pealed, deep and primordial.

'Listen to the sound of one hand clapping,' the guru said. Asananda looked at his master uncomprehendingly.

'Look inside,' Gyanananda said, pointing to the bell.

Asananda lifted the bell and peered into it. It had no tongue.

'It's a miracle, master,' the monk exclaimed in wonder.

'The bell made no noise, my son. The miracle is that you could hear its silence.'

The monk closed his eyes in meditation. Deep within him, the sound of the bell swayed and echoed, until it came to rest like a word.

The Monk and the Regretful Maid

The sound of the bell rippled through time and bloomed within his head, sonorous and calming, as if it had travelled a great distance. Its tongue hit the copper sides, slowly and deliberately interspaced with gravitas. Asananda opened his eyes. He had fallen asleep by the window of the inn. The little town was stirring. He heard the temple bell marking the morning from a hilltop across the river. He wondered idly about the priest who pulled its rope. He would have opened the door to the Lord at exactly five in the morning, sprinkled water from the Ganga to purify the divine alcove, and worshipped the idol with fire for the morning aarti. After nirmalyadarsanam – the ritual viewing of the deity still in the previous day's attire – he would have removed the clothes to wash the idol in milk and water as the holy abhishekam. Then he would have offered flowers – the malarnivedyam – and dressed the god in new garments. The sanctum sanctorum would be fragrant with the scent of camphor and sandal paste; the white smoke from joss sticks drifting up lazily, caressing the deity. The monk sighed. It reminded him of the morning rituals at Gyanananda's ashram, where members of the Order of Hope would congregate to ring bells, blow conches and sing ancient hymns. He missed the ashram. Gazing out of the window at the water, Asananda saw mild mist over the Nandakini. It looked like sadness.

'Would you like some breakfast?' a voice asked from the door behind, and Asananda turned to see his host. He nodded quickly.

'Are my friends up?' he asked, getting ready to leave for his bath in the dharamsala's ghat.

'They are gone,' she said. 'They said they will meet you on the Lost Path of the Buddha.'

After bathing, Asananda sat down to a breakfast of milk porridge, potato curry and pooris. The woman went to stand behind the half-open door after she finished serving him.

'This milk porridge is very good. Is this your home?' asked Asananda, raising a spoon of porridge to his mouth.

'Thank you,' she said. 'Yes, I live here, so I suppose it is mine.'

'Are many people staying here?' he asked her casually.

'Very few come here,' she answered in her low, coarse voice.

'It's such a large building, with so many rooms that I would've expected a crowd,' Asananda noted.

The woman shook her head.

'It's a difficult place to find,' she said. 'Only those who are meant to find it do.'

'Why, is it some sort of a magical place?' asked Asananda curiously. The woman giggled unexpectedly. In contrast to her voice, it was soft and musical.

'Perhaps. Also, this place is away from the town. In the daylight, it looks like a rich merchant's house, or one of those old palaces built by kings who once wished to own a home by the holy Ganga. It doesn't seem to encourage visitors. Common folk usually avoid the rich.'

A cloud drifted over the sun, lingered, and it suddenly felt as if they were shrouded in twilight. The monk got up from his seat and took his plate and cup to a tap in the corner of the courtyard to wash.

'Where are you off to?' she asked, receiving the cleaned utensils from Asananda.

'To Kailash, and a cave where I can find the Book of Shiva. It is my master's wish.'

'You are lucky,' she said. 'I wish I could travel too. Then I would have come with you to Mansarovar. I believe those who bathe in it are cleansed of all sin.'

Asananda looked at her without responding. The woman lowered her face. Her lip started to tremble.

'Do not distress yourself,' Asananda said. 'Sin is the path to salvation.'

'Mine was the sin of betrayal,' she said. 'It rose from fear.'

'Who did you betray?' Asananda said.

'Someone who trusted me,' the woman said. 'This house belonged to a rich merchant once ...' she began.

Many years ago, before she came to Nandaprayag, she lived in the merchant's house near Rishikesh. The merchant lived beside the Ganga with his wife and daughter. At dawn, he and his family would go down to the ghats to bathe before they set out for their morning darshan to the Ganesha temple across the Nandakini. The endless murmur of the river and the touch of cold stone under naked feet felt holy; for a brief moment, they felt they were in a time of grace; and suddenly, without fail, a vast chorus of temple bells awakened the deities sleeping in their dark chambers of solitude, the rituals inaugurating the beginnings of another day. Sleep lingered on the daughter's eyes, for she had stayed up for most of the night waiting for a silver boat and a boatman's song. Her eyes brimming with tears, the woman in the inn told Asananda about how she had informed her master about his daughter's obsession with the boatman.

'I've heard the story before,' Asananda said. The innkeeper looked at him curiously. But she did not probe.

'I did not mean any harm when I told my master about their daughter's fixation, but it brought doom upon the house,' she continued after a brief, reflective pause. 'I was concerned that if the family somehow came to know that I knew about Roopvati's love for the boatman, they would dismiss me. My life was very happy there, and I wouldn't have got a position like that anywhere else.'

Asananda sighed. Every act is part of a sieve, he thought, through which time flows. Everything is united by time.

'The boatman was murdered and my mistress disappeared with the boat. Her mother fell ill,' she continued. 'She refused to eat or drink and grew weaker by the day. The merchant was distraught that having lost his daughter, he would now lose his wife. The irony was that the mistress would ask for her bed to be placed on the same balcony her daughter had spent her nights on. There she waited for the girl to come home, freed from the spell of the sorcerer and his song.'

'He was no sorcerer, but an ordinary boatman,' Asananda said.

'Of course, you sadhus know everything,' the innkeeper's tone was sarcastic. 'If not a sorcerer, who else could have cast that spell on my mistress?'

'She cast it herself,' Asananda said. 'Most of us cast spells on ourselves. And we believe in that magic. It is the mischief of the small god.'

The woman shrugged and continued her tale.

'One dark night, when the moon was asleep and the wind quiet, I heard the mistress call out sharply from her bed on the balcony. I was sitting at her feet on a rug. I had nodded off, snug with my blanket draped over my head and body. I got up hastily and saw that the mistress had cast off her shawl, which was lying abandoned at the foot of the bed. I went to her, to calm her by gently caressing her forehead and hair. She used to have thick, black hair. After her daughter disappeared, her hair turned silver, the colour of the boat. That night, in the pale starlight, she wore a faint halo. She had propped herself on her elbow against the bolsters, and was gazing out with burning eyes into the distant darkness. With a trembling finger, she pointed towards a silver boat skirting the opposite bank. It glided silently like a phantom craft, but no song serenaded that night. I glimpsed a form at its helm, rowing, and before I could see the boatman properly, the mist rode out from the valleys to spread over the river. I heard my mistress cry out. I fainted. When I came to, she was dead.'

The woman fell silent. The sound of the Nandakini seemed louder.

'After lighting her pyre, the master wound up his business, sold his house and dismissed all the servants except me,' the woman started to speak again. 'He took me to live with him in this house, where he spent his time either reading the scriptures or simply sitting on the steps of the ghat, looking out at the water and the mountains across. Living with him was my greatest burden. One small act, a confidence betrayed for what I believed was for the better, destroyed so many people I loved. In the end, it almost destroyed me.'

'How did you cope?' Asananda asked.

'One morning, when I went down to the river to bathe, I saw my master sitting on the steps. I was hesitant, but something about the way he was sitting, and the dark patch of dew that had stained his shawl, made me drop my lota. I knew he was dead. And at that point, my life ended too. The only freedom from guilt was death. I resolved to leap into the Nandakini and swim and swim until my arms grew weary. I imagined the tiredness washing over me, lulling me as part of the river's lullaby, and all I had to do was let go. I had just begun to descend the steps when I heard a voice calling me and asking for shelter.'

'Who was it?' the monk asked.

'It was a small man, barely five feet high who was standing at the top of the steps. He looked like some merry spirit the morning had conjured. He was very fair with a potbelly and high forehead that reminded me of a dome I had once seen in a film about Emperor Akbar. His saffron overcloth was draped over his shoulders. He asked me if he could stay in the house.'

'Did he?' Asananda asked with a small catch in his voice.

'He thought it was a dharamsala for pilgrims,' she said. 'But I told him my master was dead, and there was no point in me living any more. He laughed. He had such a fine laugh. He told me not to worry and his people would take care of everything. He called out and a group of young monks dressed in white appeared. He asked them to make preparations for my master's cremation. Meanwhile, he was hungry, and could I please feed him? I took him back to the empty house and served him a meal.'

Asananda felt his blood quicken. His throat was dry.

'He stayed there for three nights and meditated on the ghats,' she continued. 'On the fourth day, when he was leaving, he said he would give me something in return for my hospitality. A blessing.'

'What was it?'

'He said that every true pilgrim carries on his shoulders the burdens of regret, sorrow and penitence. He did not want me to feel the pain of others any more. He told me that this house would be seen only by those who were meant to see it; by true pilgrims with a purpose who needed a place to rest and refresh themselves before they started out again,' she said. 'I've seen so many people walk past my gate without knocking.'

'And those you let in before us?' Asananda asked.

'There haven't been that many,' she answered. 'There was a storyteller who stayed over just a few days before you came. Before him, it was a young white man who came here, carrying a rucksack.'

'I've travelled a long way,' the young man had said. 'All the way from America. Can I come in and rest?'

The innkeeper had stood aside as he walked in, stepping on the cool flagstones, looking around him in wonder at the beauty of the house. He took in the gleaming wooden pillars of the peristyle, the marble fountain in the centre of the tessellated floor, and the intricate trellis woodwork along the sides of the roof. The woman bade him sit on one of the benches on the veranda and got him buttermilk to drink.

How long would he be staying, she had asked. The young man shrugged his backpack off his shoulders and deposited it on the floor. He sighed wearily.

'I'm looking for anyone who knew a man named Michael,' he said. 'He had come to Rishikesh from America. He was called Mike.'

'When was this?' she had asked.

'Sometime in the early 1970s. He was a big fan of The Beatles.'

The woman had laughed in spite of the sorrow she wore like a talisman keeping others away.

'In the seventies, I was an infant,' she had answered the young American. 'But there is a small Ganesha temple across the river on the hillock that looks like the forehead of an elephant. You could ask for him there. The priest is old and has seen many men on their way to the Himalayas.'

The young man thanked her. He had stayed the night and the next day he was gone before she woke up.

The Monk and the Saligram

Asananda fell quiet after hearing the woman's story. He turned over in his mind everything the innkeeper had told him.

'Did he find the person he wanted to meet?' he asked.

'I don't know,' she said. 'The young man said that everyone leaves behind something even after they die, a small piece of immortality. Like a singer or painter who leaves behind their art. Or a child who leaves behind visions as he grows up. Perhaps the young man from America was a true pilgrim. The potbellied man had told me that only true pilgrims would come here.'

'Did the potbellied man who had your master cremated give you his name?' he asked her.

'No,' she answered. 'But I asked one of the monks about him and they simply said they were members of the Order of Hope.'

Asananda closed his eyes and leaned his head back. 'O master,' he spoke to the eternal distances, 'what riddles have you left along my way even before I knew I was starting on this journey?' He picked up his satchel and staff. As he turned to leave, the woman called out to him.

'Wait, as they were leaving, the small man with the potbelly asked for me,' she said. 'He said it was not my time yet, and when it came, he would come for me. Meanwhile, he said that one day, a monk on his way to the Himalayas would reach here. He described you and left something for you.'

She went inside and returned with a small velvet packet. Asananda felt its contours; it seemed like an oblong wooden box. 'He said you should open it only when you are ready,' she told him. 'He said you would know when.'

'O Narayana! Another saligram,' Asananda turned the object over in his hands and said a silent prayer. 'First the monks, and now the master has given me an object that would free me from the bonds of my karma. A saligram that would take me to the Book of Shiva.'

His eyes filled with tears.

'Go to the temple I mentioned. Seek Ganesha's blessings,' the woman called after him. 'It's always good for a traveller to have Ganesha watch over him.'

Ganesha, the lord of the hordes. The destroyer of obstacles, who brought Parvati back from the dead, as the storyteller had told him many days ago.

Muttering a prayer, the monk walked against the flow of the Nandakini along a road that ran alongside the river, and uphill past the elephant hill. A saffron pennant flapped in the breeze from the top of the conical roof of a temple. Further ahead, the road climbed higher towards Joshimath, about a hundred kilometres away. The sun was approaching the centre of the sky, and the air became sharper and cleaner, smelling of rhododendron and river water. The river below flowed as a long whisper travelling far from the glaciers in the distant Himalayas. The Nandakini was dark and cool. Its soliloquy was soothing. He could discern the phrases of its passage as it hesitated among the rocks, yielding and then flowing around and between them. He imagined it spoke to him of the shadows of the ancient trees that fell like fluttering dark fabric patterned with swirls as it journeyed through the forests of the mountainsides. The river tasted of deerspit and fallen nests from which the young birds had flown away years ago. It smelt of hurrying leaves that had fallen when it was their time. The river held memories of melting ice, furrows the north wind has ploughed, and the golden sun crowning the peaks like gaudy helmets of gods. The gods were quiet, as usual, and the monk walked in companionable silence with them beside the river that held secrets holier and older than humanity. He did not look back. Hence he did not see his host at the dharamsala walk down the flight of steps into the river. He did not see her stepping into the shimmering water, arms akimbo and face turned to the sky, floating like a river spirit. He did not see the silver boat moving towards her, nor the potbellied boatman with a saffron garment carelessly thrown over his shoulders rowing vigorously towards her. He did not see his host surrendering herself to the Nandakini, turning sideways into the flow, exultant and free as the rower grasped her hand to pull her in. Her work was done and she was going home.

The Monk Worships Ganesha on the Hill

I t was an unexpectedly steep walk to the temple of Ganesha. Asananda crossed a narrow wooden bridge that was thrown across the Nandakini. It creaked as he stepped on each slat. The morning was melting into a young afternoon. The mountains wore a cloak of early shadow. A village road skirted a cantilevered mountain face and disappeared. The steps that led uphill to the temple from the road were cut into the grey-brown hillside. Asananda shielded his eyes from the sun and saw the form of the temple darkened by shadow, inky against the startling blue of the sky. Someone stepped out of the shadow and waved at him from the edge of the hill. As Asananda finished his climb, an old man, wearing rudraksh beads around his neck, greeted him. One rosary was looped around his wrist. Asananda assumed he was the priest.

'Coming from afar?' the priest asked.

'Going far, too,' the monk replied. 'Meanwhile, my hostess at the dharamsala across advised me to stop here and seek Ganesha's blessings.'

The priest had a typical mountain man's face, swarthy and leathery from long exposure to the sun. He had high cheekbones.

Wrinkles at the corner of his eyes radiated outward like in a broken glass pane, giving his face a gentle look. He had a wiry frame and did not seem to feel the cold; a thin shawl was wrapped around his torso. He wore white pyjamas of coarse homespun. His feet were bare. He bade Asananda enter.

The priest lived in a small shack in a corner of the temple. There were two rooms. The temple was built abutting the rock face. Asananda noticed a man, presumably the priest's assistant, squatting on his haunches and cooking something. The smell of dal wafted over to them.

The old priest sat down on a wooden charpoy, which stood crookedly on the taupe-coloured pavestones. The opaque shadow of a young cypress shivered on the sunlit stones. 'Eat with us before you go,' he invited Asananda. 'Meanwhile, would you like to worship Ganesha?'

The monk said he would.

The priest opened the old, heavy wooden door, which was banded with iron. Its oval-shaped knocker was tarnished black with age. He ducked under the low stone entrance and opened the door to a cave. The gateway was meant for a small man; Asananda had to stoop to enter the alcove. The elephant god was carved from the black rock face. Its trunk and the rotund torso had half-retreated into the stone, as if the god was longing to be part of the ancient elements again. It gleamed with holy oil. The stone would be cool, Asananda thought; the rock veined with hidden water and covered with moss in places where it was bare. The idol's eyes gleamed in the buttery lamplight below a thick smear of sandalwood and crimson on its pugnacious forehead.

The monk sat down on the reed mat spread on the floor in front of Ganesha. The god reminded him of Gyanananda, potbellied, full of wisdom and mischief.

'Do many people come here?' asked Asananda.

'Except for the locals, very few visit us,' the priest said. 'Our last visitor was a storyteller who was on his way to the Himalayas,' he added. 'It was almost night, and he was hungry and tired. I gave him food and shelter.'

'And he gave you a story in exchange,' Asananda interrupted. 'Was it about Ganesha?'

The priest gave him a keen look. He nodded and continued.

'It was a story about how Ganesha brought Parvati back to Kailash mountain ...'

Asananda settled down to listen.

The Monk and the Clever Son

Ganesha was Parvati's favourite. When he was born, Lord Shiva held a celebratory feast. All the gods attended and showered their blessings on the little boy. The only one not invited was Lord Shani, who was considered unlucky since he was the lord of eclipses. Shani's brother was Lord Yama, the king of the underworld. Accompanied by Yama, Lord Shani angrily stormed into Kailash where the baby lay gurgling in his cradle, as the gods and the heavenly beauties stood around him regarding him admiringly. Shani demanded that the baby be shown to him. Parvati pleaded with Shiva not to let Shani see the child. But the laws of hospitality prevailed. When Shani's glance fell on the baby, its head was severed, and it was killed instantly. Parvati swooned and the gods lamented and beat their breasts. At Shiva's insistence, Lord Vishnu went to the bank of the river Pushpabhadra, where celestial elephants came to bathe. He brought back the head of a young elephant, and joined it to the baby's body and Ganesha came to life. Yama, who was carrying Ganesha's spirit to his dark home, felt his arms grow heavy. To his dismay, he discovered that he was holding the gigantic soul of an elephant instead of a child's. He flew into a rage at being cheated by Shiva and Vishnu and vowed revenge.

As Ganesha grew up, other children refused to play with him. They called him a freak because he had the head of an elephant. Even his brother, Kartikeya, avoided him. Ganesha grew up a lonely boy who spent most of his time with his mother, guarding her when she bathed and running her errands. When Parvati was taken by Death many years later, when a jealous Ganga drowned her, Ganesha was desolate. He went off in search of her though he did not know the way to Yamalok, the abode of the God of Death. He passed through deserts, sleeping in the shade of cacti. But the dew fell on his lips, quenching his thirst. He passed through forests, where the elephants brought him bananas, for he was, after all, one of them. When thorns threatened to hurt his feet, the mayflower trees rained their thick blossoms down on the ground, forming a fat carpet for the child to walk on. These were the gifts the gods showered on Ganesha, for his devotion to his mother moved them. Such is the way our ancestors protect us from the perils of the shores that lie beyond the pale of death, when we seek their grace and remember them with a yearning mixed with happiness as we bring to them the warmth of our memories.

On his way, Ganesha met a mouse. It asked him where he was going. When it heard of the destination, he offered help and begged the tired boy with the strange head to take him along.

'But what can you do for me? You are so little,' said Ganesha.

'Even a little being can be of help,' said the mouse. 'Why don't you climb on my back and I will take you to Yamalok?'

'You will be crushed to death,' laughed Ganesha.

'It is not often that someone offers to help a god, O Ganesha,' said the mouse. 'Usually, it's the other way around. I hope you will not crush me with your weight as we travel along.'

'Do you know the way?'

'There are ways by which I can know the way,' replied the mouse with a twinkle in his eye.

The divine boy looked at the mouse and thought that the creature could be of use. Besides, not having any friends, he thought the mouse would be good company. So he used his miraculous powers to reduce his weight, but not his size. He climbed on to the mouse's back and off they went towards Yamalok, the realm of the dead. At every turn in the road, the mouse would look for a mouse hole. Since all mice lived underground, they were closer to the Land of Death and could hear the flow of the Vaitarna river, which marked the shadowy border between life and death. It was a river of blood, full of demonic crocodiles and carnivorous fish, which devoured sinners. Among mice, it is said that they twitter in their holes each time they hear a soul cry in agony while it is being torn to pieces as it drowns in the tides of blood. Ganesha's mouse would call out for his friends to come out of their burrows and tell them the path to Yamalok. Eventually, the elephant boy and his strange mount reached the Vaitarna's dismal shore.

A grey mist that hung over the water, like a vast shroud, obscured the river. Will-o'-the-wisps flickered over islands of skulls that dotted the Vaitarna, crowded with marooned souls. Mottled owls, heralds of death, cried mournfully in the darkness. Ganesha was frightened. The great forest on the riverbank stretched as far as the eye could see. The trees were made of bones and hair, and skeletons hung from the branches. In the dead wind, they clapped against one another and chattered gibberish. Hounds howled in the eternal night. Ganesha's heart sank at the sight of the swollen red river and the enormity of his task. The mouse sensed the unease in its friend.

'Don't worry, I have a solution,' it squeaked. 'I'll call my kith and kin. Each one of us will throw a pebble into the Vaitarna and soon we will have a bridge.'

Ganesha roared with laughter and slapped the mouse on the back. It almost went careening into the river, but fortunately the root of a tree sticking out stopped it from certain death. It looked at Ganesha reproachfully.

'Is this how you treat a friend, O Ganesha?' it asked. 'And that, too, one helping his friend find his mother?'

Ganesha was contrite. 'It's just that you borrowed this plan from the squirrels in the Ramayana and I couldn't help laugh at your cleverness,' said the son of Parvati.

'There are no new stories, only new lessons taken from old stories,' the mouse said cryptically and went off in search of his friends. Soon he returned with a legion of mice, and they began to pick pebbles, which they threw into the river. Some stood on their hind legs and heaved the larger stones into Vaitarna, while others pushed smaller ones in groups. Soon a bridge was taking shape. In the distant mist, Ganesha thought he saw his mother's form calling out to him, her hands held forward beseechingly. The mouse stopped him from jumping in to save her, telling him the demons created visions that doomed those who dared to venture into the Land of Death.

'One is always tempted by promises of love,' the tiny creature said wisely. 'Even if the tempters seek to devour your soul. Stay brave, and we will cross the bridge.'

As the mice kept at building the bridge, Ganesha and his little friend wondered how they could engineer Parvati's escape from Yamalok. For no one escaped the clutches of Yama.

'No more tricks from the Ramayana?' asked Ganesha.

'In fact, there is one that might work,' chirped the mouse. 'Far away, in the Dronagiri hills, there grows a herb named Sanjeevani with which one can defeat Death. When a poisonous arrow fatally wounded Lakshman, the great monkey god Hanuman went in search of the herb. Not knowing which one it was, he uprooted the entire hill and brought it back to Lakshman, who was revived. Get a Sanjeevani plant and your mother Parvati can be brought back to life. Let's get to Yama, and then I will tell you what to do.'

'But where will I find Hanuman?'

'Pray to the great Shiva, and Lord Hanuman will come. In the Skanda purana, it is written that Hanuman is an avatar of Shiva. Hanuman is the great ape, the First Father of man, the great ancestor of all humans.'

Ganesha closed his eyes and prayed to his father. Soon a mighty tempest rose, which made the skeletons on the opposite bank shake violently as if they were inflicted with ague. Lord Hanuman alighted from the sky and asked Ganesha what he wanted.

'O Great Father, I need to get my mother back,' Ganesha replied. 'You gave Lakshman the Sanjeevani and brought him back from death. Can you get it for me?'

Shiva's eleventh avatar, born of the sprite Anjana and Vayu, the wind god, looked at his son and smiled. He mussed the boy's hair and leapt into the air and disappeared. Soon he came back bearing a fistful of Sanjeevani plants. Since he had gigantic fists, they were quite a handful.

'You are a blessed one, O Ganesha,' said Hanuman. 'Your efforts are driven by love, not duty alone.'

Lord Hanuman disappeared and Ganesha rode his mouse across the bridge of stones.

After knocking at Yama's door, they were accosted by the demon gatekeeper who asked them the reason for their visit. 'People try to get out of here while you two wish to walk in,' said the demon. 'What do you want?'

'We've come to take something from your master,' said the mouse bravely. The demon roared with laughter. 'The master only takes, he doesn't give anything,' he said, wiping tears of merriment from his cheeks. 'This I've got to see.'

The demon led them to Yama's throne room. The Lord of Death recognized Ganesha as Shiva's son and greeted him respectfully.

'I've come to ask you to free my mother from the bonds of death. I want to take her back to Mount Kailash.'

'O Ganesha, that I cannot do, for nobody leaves this place,' Yama said cockily. 'It is the law of nature. I am the harvester of souls, not their liberator.'

The mouse, who had by now climbed on to Ganesha's shoulder, whispered something in his ear. The elephant head nodded.

'Can I ask for a boon then?' Ganesha said.

'Any boon except her life. After all, I cannot deny Shiva's son,' said Yama snidely. 'Though I cannot imagine what the son can accomplish where the father failed. That, too, a freak such as you.'

Ganesha's brow darkened with anger and Yama caught a glimpse of the power that lay within him and shuddered. 'Pray what would you like from me, O Ganesha?' he asked hastily.

'He wishes to see his mother again,' said the mouse. 'He wishes to embrace his mother one last time.'

'That I can allow,' said Yama, and summoned Parvati. She came like a dying evening. Her eyes were dark with despair in her sallow face, once so beautiful, and her black hair, shot with grey, flowed like a foaming river at night. Her lips were bloodless and pale. Seeing Ganesha, a sigh escaped her and she started forward, her colourless, feeble arms held out hopelessly. But she couldn't reach him, for the dead were forbidden to touch the living.

'You may embrace your son one last time,' Yama said. 'After all, he has travelled far,' he added with a touch of malice.

Parvati gave a cry of joy and held out her hands to Ganesha. 'Wait,' said Ganesha. 'My hands are full of these plants.' He turned to Yama and asked him to hold the sacred plants while he embraced his mother. As Parvati swept up her son in her arms, the mouse again whispered something to Ganesha. Quickly, the boy took out a Sanjeevani leaf hidden in the folds of his sarong and gave it to his mother to eat. Parvati was instantly revived. Incensed, Yama got up, lifting his hands in anger to throw the plants away and grab Parvati.

'I wouldn't do that if I were you,' the mouse twittered. 'Those are Sanjeevani plants that confer immortality. If they touch the ground, all the dead souls in your keeping will be brought back to life and fruit-bearing trees will spring up on this cursed, barren land. Gardens will bloom and birdsong will dance in your winds. Your realm will be destroyed, there will be no balance on earth any more, and the gods will curse you. So let us go.'

A powerless Yama could only gnash his teeth. In the end, helplessly holding the Sanjeevani plants, he allowed Ganesha to take Parvati home. This is how Ganesha was conferred the title Vighneshwara – the Conqueror of Obstacles – by Shiva, for defying Death and coming away triumphant. The mouse became his loyal companion and he would ride out on it whenever he would go visiting a worshipper who needed help. As for Yama, because he holds the Sanjeevani in his hands to this day, it came to be written that any soul he takes would be reborn according to their fate.

'What a lovely story,' said Asananda, getting up from his seat in front of the Ganesha idol. It was noon, and sunlight had crept into the sanctum, climbing up and diffusing the idol's face with a golden glow. In that shining, the form of the god seemed to grow large, and emerge from the rock into which it had retreated. It looked as if something miraculous was unfolding.

The priest nodded.

'Paul, my assistant, will get lunch ready,' he said. 'Meanwhile, you can wash at the well behind the shack.'

The monk stood up and walked towards the well. He knew instinctively that here he would find something to help him on his quest for the Book of Shiva. He wondered what it was.

The Monk and the Incomplete Son

When he returned after his ablutions, he found that three low stools had been placed on a long mat. Places were set with copper plates and tumblers arranged neatly on the ground. They sat down to eat. A young white man came bearing a small bucket full of steaming dal. He placed it before them along with fat rotis piled on a plate.

'Come, Paul,' the priest said, smiling. 'Serve our guest first and then come to eat.'

Paul was around thirty. He had blond hair and blue eyes. He looked oddly familiar to Asananda.

'Sure,' he said with an American accent. 'Welcome to our small temple, sir.'

Asananda looked at Paul keenly.

'Someone told me about you,' he said. 'The woman who lives in the house across the river.'

'Oh, you stayed there too?'

Asananda nodded. They ate in silence. After they washed up, the monk rested awhile under the cypress in the corner of the temple grounds. He gave a gentle burp; the priest had fed him too well. The young man joined him. He offered Asananda a small black ball of hashish and asked the monk if he would like to smoke. The monk declined.

'It's a habit I picked up here,' Paul said, fixing his pipe and breathing out fragrant plumes of blue smoke. 'I've been around for a few years now.'

'I heard you were looking for a man named Michael,' Asananda said. 'Have you found him?'

'Michael was my dad. He played a lot of games with me and my sister Katy when we were children,' Paul said. 'It was all about clues. He would leave a map hidden under my pillow which would lead to a book I wanted to read, which was hidden somewhere in the house. Or a key to a box, which had my sister's favourite chocolates or a Rubik's cube for me. He loved puzzles.'

'Why do you feel he has left something behind? Where is he now?'

'Everyone leaves behind something. For a loved one, finding it is the secret to closure.'

Like a saligram, Asananda thought. Saligrams are not just objects; they could be anything that liberates one from darkness, changing one's life.

'My father was an accountant who had a big firm in New York. One day, many years ago, airplanes crashed into his building. Nothing was left of him.'

'Narayana, Narayana! I'm sorry. What do you expect to find here of your father's?'

'When my parents' marriage began to crumble, sometime in the 1970s, my father disappeared suddenly. Mother was tight-lipped about it, and she burnt everything that belonged to him. All photographs, letters, everything. I was in high school then, growing up, and I was very protective of my mother. I began to hate my father for what he was doing to her. I wanted to be better than him. I got a scholarship to Harvard, made it big in Wall Street later; hedge funds, the big bonuses, the Bugatti – the works. But after the Towers fell, it didn't seem to matter. I spent days looking in the ruins and the smouldering debris of any sign of him. I found nothing.'

'So where did he disappear when his marriage was breaking up?' Asananda asked.

'To Rishikesh, to find peace.'

'What did he do there?'

'I know little except that he met a guru, who told him that there was life after death, even though there are many kinds of deaths.'

'Who was the guru?'

'I can't remember the name. I know Dad wrote to Mom, but she had destroyed all that reminded her of him by the time he died. When I asked her about the guru, she couldn't remember. All I know is that he was part of some "Order of Hope".'

Asananda sighed. The guru is like fate, his actions impossible to fathom. But, like fate, whatever he did had finality.

'When was the last time you saw your father?' Asananda asked.

'When he came back from Rishikesh, he took me and Katy out for doughnuts at the place across our apartment where he used to take us when we were kids. He said he had found peace and we shouldn't worry about him. He said, even if he were gone, he would always be with us. "Just give me a call, kid," he said'.

'Did you?'

'Not for years. But I tried calling him after I heard the news on that terrible September morning. His phone kept ringing. The phone company disconnected it later, I guess. But he was never there, then or later. I used to hate him.'

Suddenly Asananda understood the purpose of his coming to the temple. Interrupting the obstacles and pleasures in every journey are moments of serendipity. Like finding the small god, walking the Lost Path of the Buddha or bringing his guru's grace to a child. It is at moments like these that a person becomes a vessel of grace. Asananda knew he was there to finish something Paul had started. He remembered where he had seen the young man before. He marvelled at the tricks fate played on people. He rummaged in his satchel and brought out the book he had purchased at the second-hand bookshop in Srinagar. He took it out and handed it over to Paul. The photograph fell out of its pages. Paul stooped to pick it up. He let out an anguished wail, part joy and part intense grief. He clutched both the book and the photograph to his chest.

'How did you find this?' he asked, his eyes overflowing, his form trembling.

He traced the name 'Michael' that was inscribed on the first leaf. He caressed the photograph, tracing the outlines of the faces captured many years ago, when the world was a happy place.

'Didn't your sister look for your father?' Asananda asked.

'She didn't hate him like I did. She used to work with him and was with him when the Towers fell. She was close to him, unlike me.'

Asananda placed a hand on the young man's shoulder. Paul's body was trembling.

'Those you love never go away,' the monk said. 'A part of them is always there, waiting for you to find. Then you rediscover them and find peace.'

Paul wiped his sleeve over his eyes. He held up the book. 'I will take this home with me to New York,' he said. 'And I will take out the empty casket that I buried, which only had some debris from

Ground Zero. Now I will place this book and the photograph in it. Dad and Katy will finally be laid to rest.'

A spasm of coughing racked the young man's body and he doubled over in sudden pain. Asananda stroked his back, concerned. Paul straightened up with a grimace.

'It's nothing, just a cough. It will go away,' he said. The shadow of a passing cloud fell over them, like the sigh of a ghost. Faraway, the Himalayas wore a stark maquillage of snow, where another book waited for Asananda.

The Monk Faces Doubts

Paul offered Asananda a lift on his ramshackle Rajdoot motorcycle. He had slipped the book inside his shirt. He would touch it from time to time to reassure himself that it was real. He lived a few miles up from Nandaprayag, in a little village on the road to Chamoli, some ten kilometres away. Asananda sat on the pillion, staff in one hand and the other gripping Paul's bony shoulder. He muttered a prayer to his master each time the bike took a precarious turn or overtook an overladen truck.

Finally, they came to the village where Paul lived. The young American offered Asananda the hospitality of his one-room cottage that made up the first storey of a ruined cattle shed, constructed with ash-grey mountain stones. He rented it from a local farmer who owned the land, but did not care to cultivate it. The fields were overgrown with weeds and bright summer flowers swayed on their slender stalks in the gentle mountain breeze.

The village was a cluster of low mud houses with quirky slate roofs that clung to the slopes, looking as if they would slide downhill any moment. The homes of peasants looked like toy houses painted bright green and white with uneven roofs of thickly packed grey slate with stone shielings where cattle were left to rest at night, safe from leopards. Terraced fields descended in steps, green and yellow with paddy and mustard crops. A slender path skipped uphill, disappearing behind a huge rock upon which stood a small temple with whitewashed walls. A saffron pennant fluttered playfully from an iron mast atop its tower, bright against the blue sky. Paul parked his motorbike at the base of a neighbouring knoll. Asananda got off the bike and gazed up at the blue afternoon.

'So many times I've felt like that bird, gliding and dipping, seeing everything from a great distance,' Paul said. 'And when I land, life would come rushing up at me, like the ground seems to a descending bird. This book you gave me has done that to me now. It's beautiful to see things from a distance, if you can see them clearly. I should thank you for that.'

'You are an escapist,' Asananda said. Paul laughed and they climbed up the uneven stone steps that led through tiny fields to a small plateau on which Paul's cottage stood. The dirt-packed yard was fringed with wild grass. Asananda set his satchel down on the veranda and stretched.

'I would like a bath,' he said. 'I feel dusty and filthy after that motorcycle ride.'

Paul walked over to the edge of the yard from which a wild magnolia tree with fat ivory-coloured flowers leaned out into space. Asananda breathed in their fragrance. In the distance, a huge valley, scarred with distant roads, lay like a green map wrapped around the mountains. A little pathway travelled down the butte through shale and grass, avoiding the small trees that interrupted its journey to a little clearing with a well. Its walls, packed with uneven stones, were mottled with lichen and liverwort. Chickweed grew in the cracks. A tin bucket, bound with a wet discoloured rope, lay on its side beside a large stone meant for beating laundry clean.

Asananda took out his spare set of clothes and a towel from his bag. He walked down to the well. As he drew water, he felt the roughness of the rope scraping against his calloused palm. The water was cold and sweet. As he poured it over himself, he felt instantly energized. He closed his eyes as he poured entire bucketfuls, feeling the dust and grime being swept away. He washed his clothes and spread them out on a cluster of rocks nearby. The afternoon's warmth would dry them soon. A small lizard came out from under a stone, stared at the monk, and scurried off.

The wind hummed a wordless lullaby in the language of leaves, and the boughs of the trees nodded and swayed somnolently. The day's warmth spread over the monk, and a pleasant weariness flowed over him; that of a traveller nearing his destination. Asananda decided to stay awhile and savour the last of the day. He sat leaning against a tree trunk. Its bark was smooth with moss, and the scent of musk rose and lilies of the valley put him in a dreamy state. He could have sat like that forever.

He thought about the sights he had seen on the way, the people he had met and the things that had been done. He had encountered much suffering, big and small. People were always trying to escape to an imaginary space where there was only peace. It was done at a huge cost, and they often did not reach the desired destination. Why did Paul have to endure such loss and pain before attaining closure? There were so many young people from the West who came to Rishikesh, Haridwar and the Himalayan foothills to experience freedom or to find a learned sage who could explain their restlessness. Was it necessary for Amogh to suffer the loss of his house, his family and wealth before reuniting with his sister? It did not make sense. What was his fault? What was god's purpose behind Roopvati's disfigurement – she who could find salvation only by drowning in the Ganga. The boy who was beaten by a mob, where was the mercy of god and the guru?

It's such a long journey. It is through a sea of suffering that he passed and what if it proved a waste of a quest? Wouldn't he have been better off at the ashram, sitting at his guru's feet, singing psalms as the dusk deepened over Rishikesh and the lights of the temple town shimmered in the darkening water like sparkling souls freed from sin? In the end, after it was all over, what if he didn't find the Book of Shiva? What if he couldn't even find the cave?

'Don't you trust your master?' a voice within him asked. 'Don't you know by now that there is a purpose behind everything he does?'

Asananda was filled with doubt. He closed his eyes and started thinking about Gyanananda and what the journey meant to him.

The Monk and the Clever Turtle

Asananda opened his eyes, feeling a presence beside him. He saw Gyanananda sitting next to him, gazing at his face inquiringly. The guru's eyes were luminous with love that judged nothing and forgave everything. He reached out and stroked Asananda's cheek gently. The monk's eyes welled up.

'Will I ever find the Book of Shiva? Am I on the right path, master?'

'One knows that only at the end of the journey,' the master said, his love for the oblique evident even in Asananda's distress.

'O Narayana! How many towns have I passed through and how many people have I met. But everywhere all I find is sadness and ugliness. Is this the path to the Book of Shiva?'

'Is that all you find? You forget how many people you have freed from misery. You forget the saligrams you have received and what you've learned about the Lost Path of the Buddha.'

Asananda hung his head in shame. He said, contritely, 'I also keep finding you on this journey, my guru, but I seem to have forgotten it in the face of such sorrow. I forgot that I find you in fragrant groves, in charnel grounds, and the flow of the river.

I find signs you have left behind in obscure wayside temples and great houses that once belonged to rich men.'

'The truth is that you are just finding yourself, Asananda. Finding your guru means finding yourself.'

Asananda thought for a while. Then he said, 'You received me when I came to you, and the first thing you asked me to do was to get you something you deserved.'

'And you did. You got me you. No guru is complete without the perfect disciple. Without Vivekananda, Ramakrishna would've been incomplete. Without Paul and Judas both, Christ would have never achieved what he set out to – on one, he built his church, and through the other, he found himself as the Christ.'

'When will the time come when I don't have to find myself anymore? When will I gain wisdom?'

'When you come out of yourself,' the master replied. 'Though there is one universe, everyone has his or her own universe. Until you have the courage to leave yours and discover the single universe that is one for all, you will not be free.'

The sun was weakening as it sank beyond the mountains, painting the distant snowy Himalayan silhouettes with a last, fierce golden glow as if defying the end of the day. The chirping of crickets burred from the thickets. A nightjar cried in the woods. A frog croaked.

The master took Asananda to the mouth of the well and asked him to peer into the water. It was dark and slats of light wiped the surface as the wind sighed.

'A frog lives in that well,' Gyanananda said. 'He knows there is a world outside. But he doesn't want to come out since he is happy where he is.'

'Is he afraid or simply ignorant?'

'Neither. For him, the well is the universe. He sees the stars reflected on the water, he sees the roots of great trees parting the brick and thrusting down, seeking to allay their thirst. The sun warms the water and the moon cools it. He has all the insects he wants to eat and no eagle can swoop down and carry him away, since the mouth of the well is narrow. He has the world all to himself, just in that little well.'

'I've heard the fable of the frog in the well, master. What does it have to do with my quest?'

'One day, a turtle came along. He heard the frog croaking about the beauty of the world. The turtle peered in and saw the frog frolicking in the water, darting at earwigs and snapping up the flies. The turtle observed that the frog seemed to be enjoying himself and asked him if he would like more water to play in. 'Where?' asked the frog. 'The sea,' replied the turtle. 'It is limitless and deep.' The frog thought for a while and declined. He had never heard of the sea. He was convinced that the turtle was tricking him. 'You're lying, there is no sea. My well has limitless water. So leave me in peace.' Years later came a summer so fierce that animals perished, trees withered, crops died, the Ganga became a trickle and the well dried up. The frog, as it lay dying in the heat, thought of the turtle; perhaps he was right, and there was a sea; if only he had heeded the advice, he would have been alive and well. Such is the nature of hope that when everything fails, one even hopes one is wrong.'

'But how was he to know there would be a sea?' asked Asananda.

'It rains everywhere, doesn't it?' asked Gyanananda.

'So what is the moral?'

'The well is the ashram,' replied Gyanananda. 'And the guru is the rain. When the disciple leaves the ashram at the guru's command, the sea of experience and knowledge awaits him, one that never dries up. The one who doesn't venture forth dries up within.'

Asananda felt someone shaking him by the shoulder. He opened his eyes. He had fallen asleep. It was twilight and the land was bathed in a golden glow. Paul stood over Asananda, a hand on his shoulder.

'You were dreaming, my friend,' he said. 'You were muttering about oceans and frogs.'

Asananda blinked and looked around for Gyanananda. There was only the hillside and the great valley that spread out beneath him. 'There was someone with me. Did you see him?'

Paul laughed. 'Unless it was a ghost, I saw nobody. You better come back with me, eat early and sleep. I'm going back to New York tomorrow. You have to go on too.'

Asananda got up, collected his clothes and staff and accompanied Paul to his cottage. In his mind, he saw Gyanananda speaking in gentle tones and felt the caress of his touch. Great masters can project themselves astrally whenever they want, he had read. Maybe Gyanananda did that to allay his disciple's doubts. Suddenly Paul stopped in his tracks and turned towards Asananda.

'Thank you for giving me the book and the photograph,' he said. 'Now I feel that my father and sister are always with me. Those you love are always with you, and those who love you find ways to make their presence felt sooner or later.'

Asananda nodded. 'You have your task to complete and I have mine,' he said 'I've to find the ocean.'

Paul raised his eyebrows. 'I thought you were going to the Himalayas,' he said. 'Aren't you walking in the wrong direction?'

Asananda shook his head. 'I seek a different sea,' he said.

Together they walked to the little cottage. Paul cooked a simple meal of lentils and potatoes and made thick coarse, chapatis with local flour. They ate in silence. Afterwards, Paul went to sit out on the veranda. Asananda accompanied him outside. The younger man looked up at the sky, brilliant with stardust.

He took out a small pouch from his pyjama pocket, shook some dry powdered marijuana leaves onto his palm, and mixed them with tobacco. He lit up and offered Asananda a drag. The monk shook his head.

'It makes me fly away from all sadness,' said Paul, blowing out a long plume of aromatic blue smoke. 'But I won't be needing it anymore. When the Towers fell and I lost my sister and my father, I felt nothing for a while. It was as if my soul was dead. It was as if I never loved anyone the way I should have.'

'The soul never dies,' Asananda said. 'It sometimes goes to sleep, that's all.'

'I forgot to mention something,' Paul said. 'I haven't got much longer to live. It's the damn crab. That's why I came looking for something that I hoped Dad would've left behind. It would have made my last journey worth it.'

'And it did,' Asananda said sadly.

'You did it for me,' Paul said, drawing a lungful of smoke. He coughed violently. When it subsided, he wiped his mouth on the sleeve of his shirt. There were spots of blood on it.

'I thought I was indestructible, when I was raking in the millions,' Paul said. 'I would look out of the huge glass window of my office and see Manhattan glistening below, alive and hungry. I felt I owned it all, and that Dad was a schmuck to walk away from such a brilliant son. I wanted him to know and be proud of me. Today, when I sit here and watch the snow glittering in the moonlight so far away, I feel I can float, and even touch the tips of the peaks. Wouldn't you want to do it?'

'I'd rather walk,' said Asananda drily. A pale moon shone, its light softening the dark shapes everywhere.

'I always dreamed of meeting the man on the moon, and would stand with my sister on the balcony of our apartment when we were kids, looking at the big fat New York moon over Brooklyn. Sometimes, it seemed so close that I felt I could almost touch it.'

'Maybe you will,' Asananda said.

Paul nodded. 'I leave tomorrow. I would like to give you my motorbike, and you could ride it all the way to Kailash. I'm sorry it's rickety and coughs up smoke when you kick the starter, but it will do the job. It would be better than walking and hitching rides.'

Asananda protested. But Paul was firm.

'No loose ends, monk,' the American said. 'You gave me something for the final leg of my journey. I give you something for yours in return. This bike is all I possess. The circle is complete.'

Asananda saw, in his mind, the first time he met Gyanananda walking down through the snow towards Rishikesh. He heard his voice asking him to go to the Himalayas to find the Book of Shiva. He thought of other circles; of a boatwoman, a lost sister, a burning bier. He looked at Paul and nodded. He got up to go inside. Time to sleep.

Then Asananda discovered he wasn't sleepy. The moonlight filled the valley like a great, calm lake. It flowed along the mountainside, a Ganga of the sky, and softened the silhouettes of the trees. The sleeping houses on the hilltops glistened with silver.

'May I borrow your book to read a bit?' Asananda asked Paul. 'I'm not sleepy.'

The young man handed it to him. He went inside to sleep. The monk rolled up his blanket for a pillow, opened the pages, which whitened with moonlight. He had read it so many times before but never tired of reading it. He rifled through the book, searching for the part he loved the best and understood the least. His master had advised him that it was better to read a book over and over again. 'There will come a point when you will understand everything, and in some cases, you will become so confused that the words will mean nothing. Either way, you have arrived at the truth.'

For the umpteenth time, Asananda turned to the page where Alexander, upon conquering India, invites learned Brahmins to a discourse. The Macedonian asks: 'Which existed first, the day or the night?'

'The day was first by one day.' This reply caused Alexander to betray surprise; the Brahmin added. 'Impossible questions require impossible answers.'

The monk kept the book down on his chest, feeling its weight and the texture of its cover. He thought about Paul's father Michael escaping to Rishikesh as his marriage crumbled. He imagined him roaming the narrow streets, sitting with the sadhus and smoking hashish, reaching the Ashram of Hope and meeting its master.

There must be a reason he left this book behind, Asananda thought. But what?

Because Gyanananda must have asked him to, the realization struck him. He examined the book, turning it around in his hands, checked the cover with its peeling laminate. He explored the pages slowly, until his fingers felt a page that seemed rougher than the others. A yellowing piece of paper, folded twice, was pasted on the back. He detached it carefully. It was titled 'For Paul and Katy' and filled with lines of neat handwriting in fading black ink. In the end, it was signed 'Michael'.

Everyone and everything leaves something of its own behind, Asananda realized. For others to seek, find or stumble upon. Such messages make up the story of man.

Asananda began to read, and as he did, his eyes welled up.

The Monk Reads Up on the Sun
and the Moon

The monk read: My dearest son and daughter, sitting in the shadow of the serene Himalayas, I realize that where you wish to go to is not always where you reach. I still don't know where I will be after my journey is over, but allow me to tell you a story, as I have done so many times before. It is of Icarus, the boy who wanted to touch the sun and died. But it has a different ending this time.

When the king of Crete imprisoned Daedalus and his son Icarus inside the labyrinth of the minotaur, the older man, who was a master craftsman, made two traps: one for the bees and another for the peacocks who were plentiful in the royal gardens that surrounded the labyrinth. The peacock was originally a monster with eyes all over its body, which Hera, the wife of Zeus, changed into a bird. The eyes became part of the peacock's feathers. Daedalus knew the eyes could see and he crafted wings for Icarus and himself with wax and peacock feathers. They tied the wings to their shoulders and flew away from the labyrinth. Icarus, being stronger, could fly higher. The brightness of the sun blinded the eyes on the peacock feathers and its heat melted the wings. Icarus plummeted into the sea as Daedalus watched in grief. But he did not die, as everyone had thought.

A Nereid – a sea nymph, the daughter of Nereus, who lived in a silver cave deep under the ocean – fell in love with him and rescued him. Her name was Oceana. She took Icarus to the cave. When he came to, he found he was lying on the lap of the beautiful sea nymph. She wore anemones in her long hair that undulated in the waves. Around her neck were necklaces of the finest coral. 'I thought I had died,' Icarus said.

'You fell from the sky,' Oceana replied. 'That makes you a god.' Icarus protested, but she would not listen. As the days passed, and they lay together in her father's cavern, Icarus felt homesick. He wanted to leave his ocean home and be with his father who had landed safely in Sicily. Above all, he longed for the sky. He remembered the feel of the air currents beneath his wings, which bore him along, played with him, sent him diving down and lifted him up again. All he wanted to do was fly, and this desire rose higher and higher until he felt the sun's fire course through his veins. He told Oceana of his need. He described the sensation of flying, its speed and lightness.

'It sounds a lot like being in the sea,' the nymph said. 'Swim with me.'

She was a creature of the water and darkness; sunlight would burn her. In his silver prison, Icarus pined for the sky. A flying fish took pity on Icarus, for it knew what it was to leap through the air, revelling in the rush of air that sped along its sides as it jumped. When Oceana had gone to save a sailor in distress, for that was what sea nymphs did, the flying fish went to Icarus. 'Go to the sea witch Hade who lives in a cave nearby,' it told Icarus. 'She has the power to give you what you want, for she gave a little mermaid legs in exchange for her voice.'

'I will give her anything if she can help me fly,' said Icarus. 'Take me to her.' Off they went to the cave where the sea witch lived. Giant sharks and moray eels guarded it. The flying fish called out to Hade, announcing their presence. She swam out of the cave, larger than a baby whale. Her white hair spread and swayed behind her in the currents. Black tentacles below her waist rippled in the water. Seeing Icarus, she cackled and rubbed her hands together, making a school of tiny, striped bass speed away in alarm. 'What can I do for you, son of Daedalus, who is loved by Oceana?' she snapped.

'I want to fly,' Icarus replied. 'Here I'm trapped in a cave. I feel smothered by Oceana's love, for it ties me down. I can't see the sky or feel the sunlight. Me, who had flown as high as the sun before I fell.'

'It was not the sun that was the reason for your fall, Icarus, it was your pride,' chortled Hade. 'You felt powerful when you touched the sun, didn't you?'

'Yes!' cried Icarus. 'And I would do anything to touch it again, even if I were to fall again. For one who has touched the face of the sun, and is doomed never to touch it again, what are the pleasures of love?'

Hade nodded and scratched her head with one black tentacle thoughtfully. 'Oh you will fly again and feel the sunlight, but you will have to give me something in return,' she cackled.

'Anything,' cried Icarus. 'Ask anything of me, but let me feel the air beneath my wings again.'

The witch looked deeply into his eyes and demanded, 'I want your soul.' Icarus was filled with reckless joy at the thought of flying again and touching the sun. He agreed instantly.

Hade muttered a few magic words and a huge whirlpool formed around Icarus. As it spun him round and round with dizzying speed, Icarus felt something leave him with a tug that shook his very core. He felt a vast emptiness grow within him. Then the emptiness left him, too, and he could not feel anything at all. All that glowed within him was the knowledge that he had touched the sun with his wings and he would do it again. Hade muttered some incantations and a sea monster came bearing a tray. On it were two green, long wings made of seagrasses, woven around white whale ribs to which two shark fins were attached with the legs of an octopus. Hade chanted a spell and the wings magically attached to Icarus's shoulders. She nodded to the flying fish. 'Take Icarus on your back and let him fly,' she said. With a whoop of joy, Icarus leaped on its back. As it rose in the air, Icarus flapped his wings and was airborne.

He thought he saw Oceana's face looking up at him through the froth of the waves, as a ship floundered among the rocks. They were full of fathomless sorrow. But Icarus felt nothing, since he was empty inside. As he rose into the sky, a tempest was building up. Dark clouds frowned down upon him and the wild swings of the gale tossed the flyer about. The sky was obscured with darkness that shut out the sun, and the storm threw a great veil of blackness over him.

Icarus, not knowing where he was bound, flew on. He guessed the sun was hidden behind the clouds. As he climbed higher, he felt a force pulling at him, forcing him to fly upward faster. He looked up and saw a great white orb looming above him, cold and pitiless. It was sucking him in, and the force field of its gravity was crushing his wings, as he was being pulled inward. Far below, he saw the ocean's green arms rising and falling in attempts to grab the orb. In a panic, Icarus fought the pull, trying to dive down all the way back into the safe arms of Oceana, but it was too strong for him. As he crashed into the surface of the moon, he saw the brilliance of the sun beyond the dark curvature that loomed over him. Its light was cold now, white like the hair of the sea witch. He who had sought the sun had found only the shadow of the sun.

Those who look at the full moon can see the form of Icarus on its surface spread out like a patch, his wings lying crushed on either side.'

Asananda felt Paul beside him. The young man yawned and stretched. 'I couldn't sleep. I'm so excited about going home,' he said. Wordlessly, Asananda handed him the sheet of paper.

'The man on the moon, who sold his soul to fly,' said Paul after reading it. 'What did Dad mean by this story?'

'One who is consumed by an overwhelming experience will pay any price to recapture it, like Icarus wanting to fly and touch the sun again,' Asananda replied. 'Once he experienced it, nothing would stop him, not even the love of Oceana, who saved his life. He even made a pact with the devil. I suppose Michael meant that fulfilling ones desire, however powerful, is not enough. It's more important to know where home is in the end.'

'He did come home from Rishikesh,' Paul said thoughtfully. 'Dad was always a restless man, pursued by his demons. He wanted to escape everything, his marriage, us, his life in New York. Then something happened in Rishikesh and he came back to us.'

Asananda closed his eyes and imagined the American sitting in the sun-dappled shade of the Ashram of Hope, listening intently to what Gyanananda was saying. He tried to catch the words scattered in the winds of time, but couldn't.

'No journey ever ends where it's supposed to,' Paul said, blowing a smoke ring, which dissolved lazily in the air. 'But both of us have a long way to go. May I ask you for a favour?'

Asananda nodded.

'On your way, take the path that goes downhill and you will reach a lake. Locals believe bathing in it makes you enlightened. But it's obviously not true, because I've bathed in it.' Both laughed. 'Beside that lake is an ashram. In it lives someone I call the lady of the lake. She is wise. Would you please say goodbye to her for me?'

Asananda reached out and clasped Paul's hands in his.

'I promise I will.'

'She is special,' Paul said. 'When you meet her, you will know. She taught me the greatest lesson of my life.'

'What is it?'

'You will know; maybe she will teach you too. But I haven't fully thanked you, monk.'

'For what?' Asananda asked. 'With the mobike, we are quits.'

Paul shook his head. 'No, I haven't thanked you for returning my soul to me.'

A cloud drifted across the face of the moon, obscuring the distant smudges.

The Monk Meets the Abbess of the Lake

When Asananda woke up, Paul was already gone, leaving behind the lingering smell of cigarettes. The motorcycle was parked in front of the cottage. The monk clambered on and kicked the starter. He had driven bikes in another life, back when he wore a uniform. The motorcycle coughed reluctantly, hiccupped and let out a black, foul-smelling fume. The monk revved the engine, pleased at the thought of riding all the way to Badrinath on the bike. He remembered the days he would ride the army issue Royal Enfield, the wind biting his face and the powerful engine throbbing between his legs. Paul's was an old bike, rusted in places but it had a sturdy heart. Perhaps he could take the hiking trails from Joshimath to Badrinath and save some miles, Asananda thought. In winter, beyond Badrinath, Asananda knew that the paths would turn treacherous. The mountain streams that rushed down from the icy peaks would freeze into long white serpents as if a curse had been hurled at them. The Alaknanda would fall silent, its waters slowly condensing into a great depth of ice. The wind would be sharp and cold, cutting through skin and bone, freezing the blood in the veins. The sky would darken with mountain storms, hanging low with gigantic black clouds that carried hail that rained down like cannon fire.

But there is still time for winter, Asananda thought as he took the bike gingerly over the ridge of Paul's yard, the tyres biting into the gravelly footpath that twisted and turned down. He would reach Joshimath by afternoon. He could buy some fruit and sit somewhere he could hear the mighty roar of the Alaknanda meeting Dhauliganga, as it swallowed every river on the way down to becoming the Ganga. He was looking forward to seeing the oldest tree in India, the Kalpavriksha, which was planted by Adi Shankara – the first Shankaracharya. He wanted to meditate beneath it, the way the great sage had more than two thousand years ago to become enlightened. But the temple authorities had barricaded it with the usual ugly metal fences to prevent others from doing the same.

As Asananda drove down the stony path carefully, he stopped in places to admire the view. Below him, the valley was a vast lap of green. The hills rode down in quartered slopes and little ridges upon which the houses of farmers presided over the land below. Asananda could see the valley covered with the violet shadows of the foothills he had crossed and the great Himalayan ranges on the other side he would soon pass into. In the middle of the valley lay a great lake.

'It looks like a woman sleeping on the grass,' Asananda thought. The bike bumped over the rough path, often threatening to slip as it negotiated muddy trails widened by jeep tracks. The hill slope ended and the monk rode through a vast green meadow that led towards the lake. The sun was already shortening the shadows as it continued its ascent. From beyond where the lake line lost itself beyond a giant banyan tree, strains of a song danced in the wind. He could reconize snatches of it; it seemed like a hymn to Krishna. On a little isthmus at one corner of the lake, a temple slumbered under leafy oak trees. A group of women were washing clothes on its shore. Their heads were shaved in the manner of Hindu nuns. A bundle of wet clothes were heaped on a large stone slab. A young woman was scrubbing a garment on the surface of a washing stone that jutted out into the water, while her companions were wringing the water off clothes and drying them on the grass; but her head wasn't shaved like the others. She had thick black hair tied up in a knot over her neck. The nuns looked up at the approaching motorcycle. Asananda parked the Rajdoot nearby and alighted. The woman stopped her laundering and stood up, greeting him with folded hands. Asananda returned the greeting.

'Welcome to Santhimath, monk,' the young woman said in a low and melodious voice. 'Have you come to see our ashram and meet the Mother?'

Asananda thought she could be a singer. He imagined her strumming her tanpura like Meerabai, the renunciate Rajput princess who saw herself as the bride of Krishna and composed some of the most lyrical poetry on the blue god.

'Which ashram would it be?' asked the monk.

'Where the Mother lives. I'm sorry I can't take you there right now because I've to finish washing these clothes. If you walk around the lake, past that old tree, you will reach the place where we nuns live,' she said, pointing a slender finger in the direction of gigantic banyan tree that stood meditating on its reflection in the lake. Occasionally, a plop sounded when a carp leaped and dived. She resumed washing the clothes, dipping them in the water, beating them repeatedly on the rock and rinsing the soapsuds in the lake.

'Is the Mother your guru?' he asked, puzzled.

'The ashram has only gurus, including me,' one of the older nuns answered. 'There is only disciple there. The Mother.'

Asananda was mystified and amused at the same time. He hid a smile behind the back of his hand. The young woman frowned.

'Are you making fun of us, monk?' she asked, standing up, her hands on her hips, knuckles closed. She wiped the sweat off her forehead.

'Who me? Never.'

'Do you find it funny that a young woman like me can be a guru? Why don't you go to the ashram and find out for yourself?' she said, her back to him.

Asananda started towards the ashram that lay beyond the bend in the road. 'You might want to wash before you go in, monk,' a nun called out. 'The men's bathing ghats are over that way.'

Asananda nodded. As he stepped on the cool stones of the ghat, wrapped in thin films of water, he thought how tranquil everything was. The lake was fringed with pines and date trees that grew thickly side by side between the spaces where old banyan trees let down their tresses. Deodars stood with the gravitas of warriors guarding the sacred lake. The pine-wrinkled hills were like sentinels, casting dark green shadows on the water. The vegetation was dense, coloured with forest flowers and lemon bushes. Wild lotuses slept on the surface of the lake, visited by curious dragonflies. Asananda immersed himself in the water and swam a few strokes around the bathing area. The valley was still except for the sound of the women slapping clothes on the washing stones. A temple bell pealed, deep and clear, swimming across the surface of the lake and returning as an echo. The sound of clothes being washed ceased as the bell's sound spread and resumed after it was quiet again.

Asananda wondered how the young woman came to be a part of the ashram. Many old women in ashrams were abandoned widows. Some were tired of life and sought to find peace. But the young woman seemed to be in her early thirties; too young to be a guru. Maybe she was having him on. I would find out soon enough, he thought. Let me go to this ashram of the gurus she speaks about.

As he walked along the lakeshore, Asananda felt rested; the bath in the cool water had refreshed him. He was also feeling slight pangs of hunger. The song he had heard when he reached the lake became louder.

Yiththam Nandanidesata schalitayoh Pratyadhvakunjadrumam Radhamadhavayor jayanti Yamunakule rahah kelayah.

Asananda translated the words in his mind, 'He paints the entire canvas with dark colour. The sky is black with dark clouds. The woods have become dark with Kanugu trees. It is night. The Yamuna, which flows there, is also dark.'

Humming wordlessly the song of Krishna, he stepped through the gate. The ashram was a quadrangular building built around a large sand-filled square. The veranda of the peristyle was mottled with shadows. Asananda saw women in white swaying in the gloom; it seemed as if they were dancing. Their limbs moved to Krishna's music; their gestures flowing in an unseen tide. To see better, Asananda walked towards the giant oak, which grew in the middle of the quadrangle over shrines to various gods.

'These are hill gods, old pagan ones nobody except the villagers here remember,' a voice said at his elbow, startling him. It was the young washerwoman. She set the basket of laundry down beside her. Her oval face, framed by thick curly black hair, wore a soft expression. But something in the set of her lips told him she was also a woman with a strong spirit.

'The small gods,' Asananda murmured. 'They are everywhere.'

The woman gave him an odd glance, but chose not to speak. From the left edge of the quadrangle rose a small white tower belonging to a temple that was part of the complex. A red pennant and buntings fluttered in the breeze and red, holy cloth was wrapped around its brass mast. From within came the sound of bells, marking the end of afternoon prayer. Asananda saw a small figure in white emerge through the temple door, taking graceful dancing steps. The young woman folded her hands and softly called out, 'Mother, this monk has come to see you.'

The old woman paused. He noticed the startlingly white hair that showed from beneath the cotton hood of her white sari. He was reminded of Himalayan snow. She was very fair. Her face was round like a pale moon. Her forehead was smeared with ash. Her lips were compressed as if she was trying to suppress a smile; her dark, small eyes crinkled with the effort. She was frail; Asananda felt he could see the redness of her blood thrumming under her fragile skin. But her voice was surprisingly strong, like that of a young woman who laughed a lot.

'Well, well, have you brought Paul with you? It's been a while since I saw him,' she asked. Seeing his startled expression, the old woman laughed.

'I may be old, but my hearing is still keen. I heard his motorcycle from far away. I recognize the sound of Paul's bike, for he is the only one who comes here on a vehicle that old.'

'Paul is gone,' Asananda said. 'He gave me his motorcycle. He has gone to finish an important task.'

'So Paul found what he were looking for, after all.'

Asananda was surprised by her clairvoyance.

'You were the messenger, weren't you, who brought him what he wanted?' she asked the monk.

'Not really,' said Asananda. 'I only returned to him what was his.'

'I know Paul's story,' the abbess said. 'Always running away from something or running towards something. He just can't stand still.'

'He had much to be restless about,' Asananda said.

'Until now?'

'Until now.'

'It's important to learn to be still,' she said. 'Paul wasn't sure if he loved his father or hated him. One has to choose what to love and one hopes god gives us the wisdom to make the right choice. Or else, you will constantly be running between one love and the other.'

'How can you choose what to love?' the monk asked.

'You have to learn to first love yourself,' she said. 'Otherwise how will you find the small god to show you the path to love?'

Asananda was not surprised that the abbess knew about the small god. The whole universe seemed to be a conspiracy of the wise. He was beginning to understand Gyanananda.

'What is the path to love?' asked Asananda.

'For us it is the dancing path,' the abbess replied. 'The dance of the gopis in the garden of Vrindaban celebrates the beauty of Lord Krishna, the greatest lover of all time. The world is made up of desires and each gopi is a desire that seeks to consume a part of god. In the fire that is the blue god, all desires become ash, for he is the flame that draws us all to him.'

Asananda thought of Krishna and the garden beside the river Yamuna and the women who desired him dancing to the strains of his flute.

'I desire to see the dance of Shiva,' Asananda said.

'You can't love god without desiring him,' the abbess said. 'What else is the cosmos except the dance of the gods?'

From the veranda, one by one, the dancing figures began to step gracefully into the courtyard in perfect rhythm, their hands folded in obeisance and movements guided by some unseen celestial choreographer.

They encircled him, their feet creating the music of the earth as they danced. The rhythm enveloped him, and the abbess took him by the hand and together they danced late into the night as the music of Krishna's flute enveloped the night and became one with it. To the monk, it felt like Shiva was also dancing, far away on the crest of Mount Kailash with his eternal love, Parvati.

The Monk Reflects on a Story

In the morning, the abbess asked Asananda to accompany her to the lakeside. The young woman walked behind them. They came to the old banyan tree stooping over the water. The reflection of its thick crown and heavy, overhanging roots looked like a mass of shadows. Occasionally, silver ripples disturbed the image.

She stroked the gnarled trunk thoughtfully. It was ash-grey, mottled with white. Thick roots girdled the trunk.

'A wandering storyteller once told me that it wasn't always a tree,' she said. 'It was once a young man who loved himself too much.'

'Tell me the story,' he requested her.

'It's a story about desire and stillness. Centuries ago, there lived a water nymph in this lake,' she began.

The nymph had long dark hair that fell to her waist, adorned with water lilies. Garlands of vines and berries covered her nakedness and a string of cowrie shells encircled her waist. Her companions were the birds that sang from treetops, the deer of the forest that came to drink from the lake, and the rabbits that slept on the moss to keep warm. One day, as she was sitting by the lakeside and combing her hair, she heard the neigh of a horse and the jangle of bells. It was a hunter on his way home, with bunches of quail, wildfowl and other game birds strung over the pommel of his saddle. He rode a huge white horse and wore a white cotton tunic and red leather boots. He carried a bow and a quiver of arrows on his back. His head was held erect and his black hair was swept back from a wide brow and held in place with a braided band. He had large, lustrous eyes under wide, arching eyebrows. His lips were thin and red, and he was humming a tune in a low melodious voice. He carried himself as if no one mattered in the whole world except him. A little chipmunk that had leapt on to the nymph's shoulder muttered nervously that the hunter was returning home from his hunt and they should disappear immediately – 'in case he saw us and captured us,' according to the chipmunk. But the nymph did not hear. She was gazing at the hunter with wide, shining eyes. Her lips were parted and her fragrant breath was carried away by the wind; the hunter paused, as if he had smelt something, looked over his shoulder, and rode on.

'He is the most handsome man I have ever seen,' thought the nymph, whose name was Nishabda or the Silent One. This was because she did not have a voice and hence couldn't speak. Still, she called out to him, but he couldn't hear.

She slipped into the lake as quietly as an otter going into the water. She called out to him again, asking him to stop. The hunter paused by the lakeside; he did not hear her, only what seemed like an echo rippled the calm surface of the water. He dismounted and looked in. He thought he saw a form glide by beneath the surface of the lake. It must be a great fish, he thought. He ignored it and gazed at his image. 'How handsome I look,' he thought. 'My brow is as noble as a king's and my eyes are as bright as any god's. No wonder women are crazy about me.' The wind ruffled his hair and he took out an ivory comb and started combing it. He was a very vain man.

As he lay by the lakeside gazing at his face in the mirror of still water, he felt that the lake was enchanted and a pair of deep eyes looked up at him with great longing. In it, reflected around his face, was the sky. He saw himself as a part of it. He saw great hawks riding through his hair and the clouds pausing to smother him with kisses. The sun's brightness gave his face an aura. Suddenly he was humbled by the realization that he was just a passing face in the great journey of the universe; a speck amongst the eternal heavens. All vanity left him as he wondered why he had never seen such a miracle before; though he had seen himself in so many mirrors in so many places so many times. He did not know that it was Nishabda's love that had taken him outside himself. For that is what great love does; it frees you from selfishness and makes the world yours. But the hunter did not know that. He lay on the grass by the lake, gazing at his still, calm reflection as day changed into night. He saw the stars dusting the darkness around his face, the swirling galaxies that he was a part of and the moonlight he bathed in. Nishabda called to him, asking him to come to her so that they could live forever in the lake. But the hunter could not hear her. Though he did not know that the nymph's eyes had become part of the lake, he felt a strong pull, and could not tear himself away from the shore. He did not know he was becoming one with the universe, and was lost in meditation upon himself, which is the greatest meditation of all. Anguished, Nishabda called out to the heavens. The heavens answered her cry, as she was good and pure. 'What would you have us do, daughter?'

'I want him to love me and be with me always,' she sobbed.

'The first we cannot grant you, for he now loves himself as one who sees the universe as part of him and he as part of it. Don't you see, the One Without a Voice, that he has become your echo, looking at himself in you? But certainly, we can grant you the other wish.'

The hunter lay there for days that passed into weeks and months, under the spell of the heavens to which he now belonged. He began to waste away. No hunger or thirst touched him, for the knowledge he was filled with kept all desire away. At last he died, and a small sapling appeared in his place. Over the years, it grew to be a gigantic banyan tree that stood gazing into the water.

The abbess finished her story. She looked at the monk with kindly eyes, sewn with wrinkles at the corners.

'But why did you tell me this story?'

'Like it happened to the hunter, you love yourself the most when you realize you are part of the universe,' the abbess answered. 'And for everyone who loves you, you become their universe.'

'It's a moving story, but it reminds me of Narcissus.'

'Be that as it may, all stories come from the same source. Like seeds, they are taken by a thousand winds and scattered in many places,' said the abbess.

'Yes. I have heard many stories and it seems to me that all carry the same message,' said Asananda.

'What is that?' the young woman questioned.

'That the universe is one, and that in spite of the billions of people who live in the world, all are united by the same stories. That is the story of man.'

The abbess bent down and touched Asananda's feet.

'What did you do that for, Mother?' the monk asked.

'Because you have just become my guru,' she replied. 'Because I've learned something from you. Anyone who teaches me anything is a guru.'

Asananda's eyes brimmed over with tears.

'But you knew it already,' he said.

'Indeed, but one never gets tired of learning the same thing in different forms,' the abbess said. 'That is the miracle of knowledge. One day when you find the Book of Shiva, you will realize what I meant.'

Asananda knelt and touched her feet.

'I hope I'm on the right path,' he said. 'Sometimes I wonder if I have lost my way.'

'Anyone who walks on the Lost Path of the Buddha never loses his way,' the abbess said gently, laying an arm on his shoulder.

'Do you know about the Lost Path of the Buddha? Did Tapussa and Vallika come this way?' Asananda asked, surprised.

The abbess did not answer.

'Have you walked the Lost Path?' he asked her.

The abbess shook her head gently. 'I've danced on it,' she said, smiling.

The Monk and the Bride of God

Mystified, Asananda accompanied the abbess and her young assistant back to the ashram. She refused to be drawn into a conversation about the bhikshus and the Lost Path of the Buddha, telling him that everyone walked the Lost Path of the Buddha; only, they didn't know it. She served him lunch; he sat cross-legged on the veranda under the sloping roof lifted by teak beams and time-stained wooden pillars. The monk ate rice and dal, washing the food down with gulps of buttermilk.

'I have a request to make of you, my son,' the abbess said, after he finished eating. 'Will you take this young woman with you? Her name is Raag.'

Asananda was startled. The woman gave a surprised snort. When she found her voice, she protested that she did not want to go off with strange monks. The abbess silenced her with a look.

Asananda felt disturbed. He did not want to travel with anyone. Besides, he was a monk who had taken the vow of celibacy. A young woman, riding pillion behind him, would not be proper. As if divining his thoughts, the abbess laughed. 'You need not fear, for she has, like you, taken the vow of celibacy. There is no difference between a man and a woman unless you are aware of it.'

'Narayana, Narayana! I'm on my way to the Himalayas, to find the Book of Shiva. I wish to travel fast and light.'

'She is light, as you will discover when she climbs on to your bike,' the abbess said with a smile in her voice. She shushed the woman who had started protesting again. 'I'm sending her on a quest.'

'It's the first time I'm hearing of this,' said Raag, with her hands on her hips. 'I thought I had reached the end of my quest by coming here.'

The abbess shook her head. 'No, it's just starting, daughter,' said the abbess.

'What's her quest?' asked Asananda. 'How can I help? I've got a quest of my own.'

'Everyone has a quest. Every quest needs a guide.'

Asananda was surprised. He had never thought of it that way. He felt the guru's presence often and was satisfied with the course of his passage.

'Every person's quest is to find the riddle that unites life and death,' she said. 'It completes the circle of karma.'

'Do you have a quest, too?' Asananda asked curiously.

'Mine started many years ago,' she said. 'But one doesn't always have to bustle around for a quest. One can search for something by sitting still, too. Isn't that how the great sages find the truth?'

'How can the girl guide me?' the monk asked.

'Only the road can tell,' the abbess replied. She touched the monk lightly on his forehead. A white light blinded him. The light became a great sphere. He was at the centre of the sphere. Pinpoints of light sparked off its surface. He began to float towards them. As he moved, he saw a form emerging from the light. It was a young girl. She wore a yellow cotton garment that billowed around her. She wore an arrangement of chrysanthemum and jasmine flowers in her hair. She carried a musical instrument in her hand. She sat down and started strumming it gently. The sounds were discordant first, but as she slowly refined them, twisting and turning the knobs at the instrument's wooden end where the strings were tied, melodious notes began to emerge like nightingales released from a cage. Asananda asked her name. But no words came, and the monk knew he was trapped in a dream. The sphere expanded and the monk moved forward.

In another part of the sphere stood a blue-skinned man, playing a flute. He wore a peacock feather in his thick dark hair. He was dressed in yellow. In Asananda's vision, the music that emanated from him formed rainbows. The monk tried to get closer to the flautist but the distance seemed immeasurable. Then there was a flash of light and he saw the girl had grown to be a young woman, who was singing soundlessly, as if in a silent movie. Her song reached out to embrace the blue man. He saw shapes trying to pull her away, but her aura was so strong that the shadows receded. The monk was travelling through time; it was not a linear journey, but an undulating one: as if he was riding a catamaran. There was another flash of light and he saw the young woman grown old; her form ailing and frail, her posture drooping. But her song had grown more brilliant in the light, like a string of dancing gems that encircled the god's brow to form a diadem. Her frail fingers sped up and down the instrument's strings. She grew more and more insubstantial until she almost faded away. Suddenly, at the end of his vision, she became clearer than anything he had ever seen. He saw every line, wrinkle and flaw on her ancient face as if he was a mirror. Her hair was white and her limbs were like sticks. She raised her face to look at him. Her eyes were dark and clear like those of the girl he saw first in the vision.

The monk opened his eyes and found he was sitting on the grass beneath a wayside oak. His motorcycle was parked nearby. Raag sat a little distance away, looking at him curiously.

'I thought you would crash into a truck,' she said with a toss of her head. 'I've never seen such reckless driving; you'd make a better race driver than a sanyasi.'

'How did I get here? When did you arrive?' They were sitting on a large ledge covered with grass that overlooked the river. The mountains were softening with evening shadow and afar, in a pool of shining sunlight, floated the snow-topped Himalayas.

'You had a vision,' Raag said.

'While I was driving?' he asked.

'Well, you got on your bike, leaving me barely enough time to clamber on, and you were off like a hornet,' she said. 'I could see Mother laughing all the way behind us. I asked you to stop, but you wouldn't.'

'How come we did not meet with an accident? What was the vision I saw?'

'The Mother works in mysterious ways,' she answered. 'What did you see?'

Asananda explained. The woman looked thoughtful. 'When I was a young girl, my mother told me the story of Mirabai,' she said, 'the princess who was wedded to the lord. We still sing the hymns she wrote in praise of Lord Krishna.'

The sixteenth century poet was a princess born in Rajasthan in the royal family of Jodhpur. When Mirabai was only three, an itinerant ascetic gave her a small statuette of Sri Krishna. 'You take good care of him and love him well, little girl,' the ascetic said, placing his hand on her head. 'One day, he will invite you to join his dance. Krishna calls all those who love him to dance with him, and one day, you will complete the circle.'

'What does completing the circle mean?' asked little Mira.

'Everyone is part of a circle. When you are born, you lead an incomplete life. You die with many regrets and unfulfilled dreams. Through your many births, the Lord will help you pay off all your debts and get your due. Haven't you heard about the beautiful Radha and her gopis who sing and dance around Krishna in a circle and become part of the divine dance? One day, you will also sing and dance for the Lord.'

The ascetic went his way. Mirabai's father thought the statuette was a sign from god, but hid it from her, fearing the young child would not treat it with proper respect. But Mira had become deeply enamoured with the statue. She refused to eat until it was given to her. She vowed then that she would marry only Krishna and carried the statue with her wherever she went. She imagined she was wedded to her god and sang and danced for him. When she came of age, her parents married her off to a local prince. But she refused to sleep with him because her devotion to Krishna had only grown stronger. She would sing in front of the little statuette and dance to her own music.

'Go to that impenetrable realm! That death himself trembles to look upon. There plays the fountain of love! With swans sporting on its waters,' Mirabai sang as she danced.

But it wasn't easy for a woman in the sixteenth century to do what she willed. Her husband's family hated her obsession with Krishna. They tried to poison her, but she was unaffected. One day, Emperor Akbar heard of Mirabai's music. His court musician was the great Tansen. In disguise, they visited Mirabai. She was sitting by the shrine of Krishna. Her eyes were closed in devotion and she was lost to the world as she sang.

'You are the world's greatest musician, Tansen,' said the emperor. 'And I heap riches on you and bestow you with grants of lands and lofty titles. You can sing ragas that can light lamps with the force of your music. You can make it rain. But Mirabai's music is so sublime, it is greater than yours. Yet no lamps come to life and it doesn't rain. Why?'

'I sing for an emperor while she sings for a god,' Tansen replied. 'A god doesn't need miracles to entertain him. He is the miracle.'

Akbar was so moved, he took off his bejewelled necklace and placed it at Mirabai's feet. Her suspicious husband, doubting her chastity, ordered her to commit suicide by drowning in the Yamuna. As she walked towards the river, she heard Krishna asking her to walk to Vrindaban instead.

'You have completed your circle by reaching me,' Krishna told her. 'It's now time for you to help others complete their circles through me.'

'What does Mirabai have to do with you or me?' the monk asked the young woman.

'Mirabai had her small god and I, too, am god's bride. Or, at least, was.'

'God's bride?'

'Yes, I was born into a line of devadasis, once the most noble of castes. My mother died young and my grandmother raised me. In her heyday, she was known as the greatest singer and dancer of her time. She was even married to a prince.'

Devadasis, known as the brides of Krishna, preceded Mirabai's time by centuries. They danced for the blue god, fanned him with peacock feathers and sang his praises. The songs were put together as the epic poem *Gitagovinda*. In the golden aura of temple lights, under gigantic, black stone pillars, they danced, decked in all their finery with the irresistible allure of goddesses.

'The glory days are gone and many of our kind became prostitutes,' Raag said. 'My grandmother didn't want me to grow up into one. She would tell me of the days she lived like a queen in the castle of the devadasis on the bank of the river Banas. A bridge made of ghungroos spanned the river. On full moon nights, the king would come to a wide promontory that jutted over the river overlooking the castle. His attendants would spread costly rugs and place silk-covered bolsters and cushions for him to sit upon. They would light great torches fixed to crevices in the rock face. The king would tap the rope lightly and the bridge would resonate with the sound of bells; the first ghungroo hitting its neighbour, which in turn would hit the next one, and so on, until the night became a gigantic orchestra of bells. That would be the signal for her to come dancing down the bridge dressed in all her regalia; the ghungroos on her feet tinkling in symphony with the chanting bridge. She would dance for the king until dawn and make love to him as the sunrise warmed their bodies. Then she would sing to him of Mira and Krishna and, soothed, he would fall asleep on her lap.'

'You have a rather lurid imagination for a girl from an ashram,' Asananda remarked.

'The future is not always what we imagine it to be,' said Raag. 'But the past is what we think it is. When the circle is complete, we are free of both.'

Asananda pondered over her words and observed that she had a remarkable teacher.

'My grandmother is a wise woman. That's why she took me with her.'

'Where? To the abbess?'

'The abbess is my grandmother.'

Asananda was struck speechless.

'My grandmother says she started off as a dancing girl in her youth only to become a spiritual being in her last years,' Raag said. 'It is her path towards completing the circle.'

'Where are your parents?'

'Mother died when I was small,' Raag said. 'As for my father ...' Raag gave an eloquent shrug.

'And now you are with me,' said Asananda. 'Will sending you off with a stranger help you close your circle?'

'For my grandmother, there are no strangers, only people who would cross her path one day,' Mira answered. 'Two wise monks taught her that once.'

'Two? I thought it would've been a pot-bellied, fair man with a saffron overcloth and mischievous eyes.'

'No, he came later. When I was growing up, my grandmother didn't like the way men looked at me, and the things they hinted they wanted to do to me. We left our village, not knowing where we were going, and reached Rishikesh.'

'Why Rishikesh?'

'Because it was on the way. Doesn't one always go someplace that is on the way? At least that's what the abbess taught us.'

'What happened in Rishikesh?'

'We reached an ashram by the river where the potbellied man was the guru,' Raag said. 'He asked grandmother what she could do for him if we were allowed to live in the ashram. She offered to dance for him.'

Asananda was struck speechless. The image of a devadasi dancing for his guru made him uneasy. Sensing his confusion, Raag laughed.

'It was the dance to celebrate Krishna, one that has been taught for generations,' Raag said. 'My grandmother was giving the guru the wisdom of her lineage, her most precious possession.'

'What did the guru do?'

'He got up and danced for her in turn. Together, they danced through the night and the people of the ashram gathered around them singing the *Gitagovinda*. The guru's hair came loose as he danced, sometimes merging and separating from my grandmother's. Flames danced away from the lamps he held in his hands, and lit up my grandmother's eyes.'

Asananda closed his eyes, imagining Gyanananda dancing with the abbess.

'We stayed in Rishikesh for many years until I grew up,' Raag continued. 'One day, the guru asked my grandmother to take me to an ashram that belonged to his order, the Order of Hope. It is yours, he told her. It is there you will dance and teach others to dance.'

'Can you dance?'

'All of us can dance. Can you sing? I can dance for you, if you wish.'

'I can't sing,' replied the monk in alarm.

Raag looked at him with tranquil eyes. 'Then sing with your heart,' she said. 'The tune doesn't matter.'

Asananda was beginning to understand why the abbess had sent Raag to travel with him. He closed his eyes. He heard the soft cadences of feet tapping the ground. As their tempo increased, an ethereal melody rose from some deep wellspring within him to encompass the world; Asananda surrendered to its sweetness. The dancing steps alternated in speed and pattern before him, behind him, circling him; cajoling softly or demanding and imperious. Asananda's eyes suddenly fluttered open and Raag stopped dancing. She was laughing. It was then that Asananda realized that he was the one singing.

The Monk and the Song of Fire

Asananda sulked as he travelled with the young woman along the mountain path that girded the ascending hills.

'You tricked me into singing,' he accused her as they rode on. Raag was giving the instructions and she laughed at his words.

'You sing quite well for a monk,' she said. 'I danced for you, but you didn't even see it.'

He saw her dance in his mind, noticed the feminine curves and the flashing black eyes, the neck slender like a swan's. He felt uneasy at the proximity of her young body; he had not been with a woman for a long time. Whenever the bike took a curve, she would lean against him and her firm breast pressed against his back. He parked under a wayside tree and got off.

'I cannot do this,' he told Raag. 'Your closeness makes me feel awkward. You must find your own way from here.'

The young woman hid her smile behind her hand. 'You haven't conquered yourself yet, monk. Hasn't your master taught you how to?'

'If you are so smart, how does one conquer oneself, according to you?'

'By doing the same thing over and over again until you come to a point where you cannot distinguish between yourself and it,' she answered. 'The abbess taught me that.'

'That's addictive. It's like taking a drug.'

'There is a difference. The addict craves the drug and is never one with it. The drug controls him.'

'That's why I don't smoke the pipe of Shiva. What if I lose control?'

'Afraid of losing control, monk? I thought you ascetics were masters of self-control,' Raag teased.

'I thought I was, until you got on my bike,' Asananda said drily.

'You have to practise. When we first came to the ashram, the abbess gave me mantras to chant. Each one had to be said 1,008 times. I would chant for a while and then the repetition bored me. I would look for any excuse to get away from just sitting in one place and chanting. I discovered that going to the lake to bring water for the ashram was a good way to escape the monotony of chanting mantras. I could watch the fish swim among the shadows of the banyan tree. I could chat with the village women and play with their children. The abbess asked me how my prayers were going. I said I did them religiously, but was also busy with the important task of bringing water to the ashram. Without water, how would the nuns survive? The abbess asked me why someone else couldn't do it. Others had been carrying out the task before, so couldn't they continue? I said they were old women and I was young and strong. It was easier for me to bring the water and it would give the old nuns some relief. The abbess did not say anything.

'The next morning, she told me to bring water from the lake for her bath. I brought her a pail full of water. She asked for more. I brought water again. But her tub just wouldn't fill up. She kept wanting more. This went on until it became dark. My arms were sore, my body had become heavy and I could barely walk.

'I told her I was tired and my body was aching all over. The abbess only nodded. The next day, she sent me out for water again. This continued for many days, until, suddenly, I realized I couldn't feel the pail anymore. It had become a part of me, an extension of my arm and my body. My aches and pains were gone and I felt incredibly strong. Then it became a joy to bring water for the abbess and the ashram every day.'

'She is wise, your abbess,' Asananda said. 'But you just got used to it until you couldn't feel it anymore.'

'True. A warrior practices with his sword so much that, one day, he becomes one with it. Then he is complete.'

'So you suggest I keep riding this bike until I become one with you? Or with the bike. How ridiculous is that?'

'If we were not renunciates, I would say it is lovely. In your case, if you practice long enough, you will become one with your path and you will not be able to tell the difference between your journey and you. The only way to reach the Book of Shiva is to become Shiva.'

The monk bowed his head. It was not the first time someone told him about becoming Shiva, but it was the first time it came from the lips of a young woman.

'If you do not become one with the journey, it will make you weary,' Raag said. 'Remember the abbess telling you about the great Tansen and Mirabai? The day I found joy in bringing water, the abbess told me the story.'

Emperor Akbar had heard of a singer named Tansen whose music could make rain and create fire. He made him part of his navaratnas – the nine jewels that adorned his court and were the most talented people in the empire: the learned historian Abul

Fazal, the incisive satirist Birbal, the great economist Raja Todar Mal and others. But the emperor loved Tansen's music the most because it cast a spell on him, banishing the worries of state. Akbar instructed his architects to construct a lotus pond called the anup talab on an island. On it, they built a gazebo. They brought an orange tree from China and planted it on the island to perfume the air. Every night, Tansen would sit on rich Persian carpets under the gazebo, strum his rebab and sing for the emperor and his retinue. Hearing his songs, the emperor's daughter Meherunnisa fell in love with Tansen and married him. One fragrant night, after they had made love under the orange blossoms, Meherunnisa lay back on the deep carpets and looked up at the sky. 'It's warm tonight,' she said. 'Can't you sing Megh Malhar – the melody of the clouds – so that rain cools my body and I can make love to you again?'

Tansen took up his rebab and began to sing. Clouds gathered above, wiping away the stars and the soft, misty moon. The heavens growled and lightning flashed, cleaving the sky. It began to rain. It fell on the princess's smooth skin, on her long black hair and full, red lips. She looked up at Tansen, her eyes deepening with desire as he sang; eyes closed and oblivious to the world around him. She felt exultant that she had the power to command Tansen to make rain or fire. She held her fair hand up to his lips. He stopped singing and came out of his musical trance. The rain fell slim and long around them, on them.

'Where did you learn to do that?' the princess asked.

'My guru taught me to practise the ragas until I couldn't tell the difference between fire and water. He called it completing the circle, the union of opposites – when nothing is left but love.'

'Then don't stop singing. Sing the opposite, too, Deepak, the melody of fire, create a new melody by singing both together,' she commanded. 'I want to see the lanterns on our orange tree light up, defying the rain when you sing. I want to see if the rain can quench the fire.'

'It could be dangerous Meherunnisa, for no one has ever attempted to sing both together.'

Akbar's daughter insisted. It was something Tansen had never done before; summoning fire and water together. It was the ultimate skill, and everything he had trained for. The great musician bowed to the princess and plucked the strings of the rebab again. As the notes soared through the rain, and his voice summoned the sky, there was a great clap of thunder. The sky roared, and a bolt of lightning tore the clouds. It raced down to the island and set the gazebo on fire. Both Tansen and Meherunnisa were consumed by it. The distraught emperor mourned the deaths of his two favourite people and shook his fist at the sky.

'He courted you with his music and is this how you reward him?' he shouted at the rainclouds.

'He had summoned divine fire with raag Deepak,' said the clouds. 'The music would have, in turn, set us on fire.'

'Didn't he realize that he would die?' asked the king. 'Why did he do it?'

'He had closed the circle. All great artists seek the ultimate perfection, even as they realize their limitations as mortals. Tansen only loved two things, his wife and his music. When he called down the divine fire, immolating both him and Meherunnisa, he became one with his love and god. There was nothing more to live for.'

It's a beautiful story, the monk thought. His master would've liked it.

The afternoon was getting warm. Raag perched on a large rock under the oak. She took two apples out of her knapsack and tossed one to Asananda. 'Eat,' she said mockingly. 'If you aren't strong enough, how will you find the Book of Shiva?'

The Monk and the Harvest God

Raag instructed him on the path they should take. Some mountain roads were wide and paved with tar; some the rain and small landslides had broken in places. At one point she asked Asananda to turn into a village path that skirted the scree on the hillsides haphazardly before careening down to a vast green valley.

'What is your quest, Raag?' Asananda asked, glancing back at the woman who sat behind him, clutching his shoulder with one hand and the other gripping the seat. Strangely, he was not disturbed by her nearness anymore.

'The abbess said I have to pass the doorway to myself, whatever that means.'

'I suppose you will know when you see it,' Asananda said. He felt her shrug behind him. As he carefully guided the bike down through the shrubbery, almost slipping on the shale at places, he got the strange feeling that they were travelling back in time. The verdant hills seemed familiar; a moustache of cloud on one taunted him comically. The Himalayas were sometimes behind them; at other times appearing ahead as the bike carefully negotiated the sharp curves cut into the rock.

'I know where I'm going,' Asananda told Raag. 'But I'm mystified about your destination.'

'Ride on, monk,' she laughed. 'I'll reach there all right.'

'I hope we get to Joshimath by sunset and find a dharamsala. I can sleep anywhere; in a cave, a bus shelter or under the staircase of a hotel. But it's not safe for a young woman like you.'

'The Mother looks after us all,' Raag said cryptically. The afternoon was still young and the air felt crisp on their faces. The abbess had made the girl his guide and had promised him that she knew all the shortcuts to Joshimath. Raag supposedly even knew of dharamsalas in small towns and monasteries that were hundreds of years old and where they could get a warm welcome. Asananda no longer knew where he was going. He drove on, trusting Raag to take him to the right place.

'I thought Joshimath was close by, and we should have reached there a long time ago,' he said uneasily.

'This is a shortcut. But it's only about forty-odd kilometres from Joshimath to Badrinath,' Raag answered.

The path downhill was narrow and almost vertical. Asananda asked why they were going down when they had to go uphill. 'Look, you're slowing me down. With all respect to the abbess, I think you should get off the bike at some village on the way. From there it should be easy to find your way back. I have to reach Badrinath before nightfall,' Asananda told Raag.

She was quiet. The path levelled and they were bumping along a cart track in the valley. It widened as it plunged into the space between fields; they passed large green meadows and grazing cattle. Cowbells tinkled in the wind. Clusters of oak trees threw down large pools of cool shade. A crow cried. A squirrel darted across the bike's path and Asananda braked sharply. Raag giggled. The monk frowned.

They rode on until they reached a village. It was a small cluster of mud houses that stood huddled close to each other. Their walls were painted bright blue and the roofs were of uneven grey slate. Under a large peepal tree lay an old man on a string charpoy, lazily smoking a hookah. The smoke drifted up as fuzzy interrogation marks. In the breeze, it smelt rough and pungent. Asananda sneezed. Raag gave him a few thumps on the back.

'You're the only sanyasi I've seen who doesn't smoke. The rest are all crazy about Shiva's substance. Including some of the sisters in my ashram, if I may say so,' said Raag laughing. She seemed to laugh a lot.

Asananda shrugged and parked the motorcycle under the oak tree. Raag hopped off and approached the old man. He peered at them suspiciously through a pair of thick spectacles miraculously held together with a piece of string. He took in Asananda's robes and satchel. He examined the young woman with a critical eye.

'I see that you have brought him here, daughter,' he spoke, looking at Raag. She looked puzzled.

'Grandfather, you mistake us for someone else,' Asananda said. 'We are on our way to Joshimath.'

'I'm never mistaken when god sends me a sign,' the old man said, gazing intently at Asananda. 'Besides, Joshimath is quite far away, you are going in the opposite direction,' the old man said, waving his stick in the direction behind him. Asananda was taken aback.

'I thought you knew the way,' he told Raag with asperity in his voice.

'Isn't it fun to be lost?' asked Raag cheekily. 'As your guide, I must however tell you that we are on the right path.'

'Wait,' the old man said. He kept his hookah aside, heaved himself up and sat cross-legged on the charpoy. He said, 'god never acts without purpose, though, most of the time, we discover it only later. I know why you came here, monk. Tonight is the festival of the harvest god. Unless we please him, the crops will fail. Our priest is sick, maybe dying. Please fill in for him.' He folded his hands and looked beseechingly at Asananda and the girl. Asananda drew Raag aside. He was very angry.

'You know very well that I cannot stay back and stand in for a priest when I've to reach Joshimath today. Tomorrow I leave for Badrinath and Kedarnath.'

'You will, my dear monk. All he is asking you to do is pray for a good harvest. And isn't that what you want, too? A harvest of grace?'

Asananda glared at Raag. She met his frown with equanimity. She grabbed his hand and took him to the old villager. She knelt and touched his feet. The old man placed his gnarled hand on her head and blessed her.

'Show me the shrine,' Asananda said with a sigh.

Together, the three of them walked towards a little grassy knoll where the village ended and the fields began. A small stone shelter stood with its back to them, facing the mountains that guarded the valley. A granite wall, broken in places, rose and dipped along the uneven ground, which was covered with wild grass. A frangipani tree in bloom scattered its perfume in the wind.

A gaggle of village children and women followed, keeping their distance as the monk and the young woman accompanied the old man, who was hobbling towards the shelter. It was a large grotto with an entrance closed by a low wooden door that hung on iron hinges.

'The harvest god's shrine is inside,' the old man said. 'The puja is to start at night, just before the moon appears.'

The women and children had come closer and now stood in a semicircle around the three.

'Tonight's the full moon, the harvest moon. It is the time when the god and his three guardians wake from their six months of sleep to dance with us,' the old man said. 'But we need a priest to show them the way to reach us.'

'How do I do that? I don't know the ritual,' said Asananda.

'You have to light the lamp and bathe the god in oil,' said the old man. 'And chant the great harvest mantra.'

'How do I find the mantra?' asked Asananda in confusion.

'It is written inside the grotto, above the god's head. Until then, you rest. You will be awake all night.'

Asananda silently cursed Raag for bringing him to the desolate village where he had to play priest to some strange god, when he could be peacefully riding towards Joshimath and Badrinath on Paul's motorcycle instead. The hills were full of pagan gods and rituals, which he knew little of. Each village and temple had its own diety: one that governed the rain, the wind or kept the foxes and crows away. How was he to tell which one was the harvest god?

When twilight arrived, the monk accompanied the old man to the grotto. Raag had vanished, but he had no time to look for her. Heaps of frangipani, golden showers and red hibiscus flowers were neatly heaped on one side of the temple door. On the other side were packets of joss sticks, incense and a large copper pan full of sacred ash.

The mountains glowed in the remains of the sunlight, their edges luminous with the farewell of another day. Standing on the broken wall and looking out, Asananda could see the fields stretching away, pregnant with wheat and corn, sashaying slowly in the valley winds. The dusk deepened the hills, shading the wooded sides. It teased the shadows. A flock of storks flew through the gathering darkness, their graceful white wings rose and fell in slow rhythm. The sky was clear and the early stars had begun winking their presence in the soaring cobalt-coloured arch above. There was excitement in the air and Asananda could sense the restlessness among the small crowd of villagers. Suddenly one of them shouted and others followed suit. They looked up at the sky and pointed towards the great pale moon, which had just appeared from behind an indigo cloud, clapping their hands and laughing. The sky had begun to lighten. The old villager told Asananda to open the door of the grotto when the moon came out.

'Wait,' he heard Raag call from behind. He turned and saw her leading a small procession of village women towards the temple. They were bathed and wore fresh clothes; Raag had borrowed a skirt and blouse from someone a size bigger. She looked like a little girl. For a moment, Asananda forgot his irritation and a great affection welled up within his heart. The village women bore copper pitchers brimming with water on their hips. The vessels were adorned with mango leaves, a sign of auspicious events to come. They moved in circles on the mud-paved earth, scattering handfuls of water in what was obviously a purification rite. Raag emptied her pail over Asananda's head. He spluttered and almost swore. He shivered as the wind rubbed against him.

'That's called a bath, monk. You need to purify yourself before you start your worship,' she said. Asananda chose not to answer.

The moon rose to its full height, its glowing halo lightening its pale province of the nightsky. The old man opened the wooden door of the grotto. Asananda stepped inside. The moonlight could not penetrate the shadowy interior. Raag passed him an ancient brass lamp brimming with oil. Asananda lit it. The

buttery light turned the interior of the grotto golden, banishing
the ancient shadows.

There were five idols inside. In the middle sat a stone man; his
eyes closed upon his frayed cheeks, a gentle smile on his full lips.
His hair was gathered in a hive-like fashion and tied above his
forehead. His pendulous earlobes hung low. His large hands lay
clasped on his lap, holding a huge bushel of wheat. Three smaller
idols were arranged around him. The first was a frail old bull.
Asananda was amazed at the detail the sculptor had managed to
coax out of the stone: the protruding bones that poked through
the wrinkled skin and the debilitated posture of the beast; the
miniature bull, with its withered flanks, splayed legs and bowed
neck, looked as if it was battling some terrible bovine disease.
The next idol was the bull which had collapsed kneeling on the
ground, its head hanging down and horns touching the uncaring
earth. Its glazed eyes held a wide stare, and the gasping mouth
was covered in froth. The third idol was of the same bull; it lay
on its side, eyes closed and thin legs stretched out; the sense of
stillness the nameless sculptor had imparted to the form of the
supine beast gave it a terrible sense of finality.

Asananda leaned forward and read the words carved into the stone
in a semicircle, like a halo around the god's head. The language looked
familiar; it was not Sanskrit, but some variation. He read, *'Buddham
... Saranam ... Gachchami ... Dhammam ... Saranam ...'* The three
stages of refuge in Buddhism. *'Buddham saranam gachchami,
dhammam saranam gachchami, sangham saranam gachchami.'*

Asananda recognized the Buddha and his muses. He also
realized that the three stages of the bull were the three sights the
Buddha saw when he ventured out of the palace gardens with his
charioteer Chandaka, which eventually took him on the path of
renunciation, suffering and wisdom. The ageing bull, the diseased

bull and the dead bull. Above it all, sat the image of the ascetic, presiding over the three implacable stages of life. Outside the temple, the villagers began to chant, their chorus rising in the air in unfurling octaves, vying to reach the harvest moon. '*Om muni muni maha muniye soha*,' they chanted the Shakyamuni mantra of the Avalokiteswara; the Gautama; the Buddha.

Asananda felt the chant cutting through the harvest of his consciousness like a great scythe. He knew with unshakeable faith that he had discovered the Lost Path of the Buddha. As he chanted the simple Buddhist prayer again and again, its meaning unfurled within him in glorious simplicity.

> *Buddham saranam gachchami*
>> (I take refuge in the Buddha, who is myself.
>>> The Buddha is the Great Being and
>>> the small god alike.)
>
> *Dhammam saranam gachchami*
>> (I take refuge in the truth, which is
>> the consciousness of the Universe and
>> that of all beings in it, big and small.)
>
> *Sangham saranam gachchami*
>> (I take refuge in mankind, because
>> without it, I am nothing.)

As the realization deepened, Asananda felt Raag's presence like the warmth of a lamp. He forgot his anger at not being able to proceed to Joshimath. He was filled with a great sense of gratitude towards the young woman. She met his eyes with the smiling gaze of a guide.

'I didn't know what the abbess meant when she said that every quest needs a guide,' Raag said. 'I'm sure the Buddha passed this little village on his way to Gaya and was given food and shelter by the ancestors of these villagers. As a blessing, he gave them a miracle. And I too am blessed to travel on the Lost Path of the Buddha with you.'

The next morning they continued towards Joshimath.

The Monk and the Four Sightings

Through the cool morning with the wind in their faces, Raag and Asananda drove along a mountain path in the valley. Raag was giving directions. The monk did not ask her where they were going; after the previous day's experience, he was content to go where she asked him to. He knew Joshimath lay ahead, and he was nearing the end of the journey.

As they travelled, the landscape became familiar: the green-ribbed mountainsides, the vegetation turning a different green, of wild palm trees and rhododenderons. The smell of fresh water was in the air. As they passed a cluster of oak trees and crested a small hillock, Asananda drew his breath sharply. The lake lay below them, vast and calm. A banyan tree stood on its shore, and even from the distance, he could make out it was huge. He stopped and turned towards Raag.

'Why are we back?' he inquired sharply. 'This is not the way to Joshimath.'

Raag got off the bike and stood for a while, looking out at the water. She sighed.

'The abbess told me I would help you find something, and I did,' she said. 'She wanted me to bring you back for a final farewell. Can we go now?'

Asananda exhaled and nodded. He had given up trying to understand Raag and the abbess. The ride down to the valley was short. As they drove towards the ashram, Asananda saw two familiar figures sitting under the tree. Their saffron robes looked freshly laundered and their faces were brighter than he remembered.

'Tapussa, Vallika! The Buddha be with you!' Asananda greeted them with enthusiam, for he did not think he would ever see them again. 'What are you doing here?'

'So you found the Lost Path of the Buddha,' Tapussa said.

'He was meant to,' said a soft voice from behind and Asananda turned to see the abbess. He touched her feet.

'Guru Gyanananda told us you would,' Raag chirped. 'He said that you would wander a lot, see many strange things and hear many stories which will all take you on the Lost Path of the Buddha. It will lead you to the Book of Shiva, he said.'

Asananda was stupefied.

'How do you know that?' he asked.

'The Mother told me that when she saw you for the first time,' Raag shrugged, gesturing towards the abbess.

'Do you know Gyanananda?'

'No. But he is the Mother's guru and she is his. I've heard of his powers from her.'

'When did he come here?' he asked the abbess.

'Many years ago,' the abbess replied. 'He came to visit after he gave me this ashram. He stayed here for a while. When he was leaving, he told me that a student of his would pass by. He described you. Then you were not a sanyasi, but an ordinary searcher.'

Asananda felt giddy. His master seemed to have planned his entire life out for him, from the moment he met him on the way up to the cave where he was to spend many years in meditation. Meditation was born out of a desire to be alone, he knew. After the war, he desperately needed to be alone.

'Did you know my guru?' he turned to Tapussa.

'We are on our way to meet him,' the bhikshu answered. 'He is the last stop on the Lost Path of the Buddha.'

'I'm not ever sure I am on the path,' said Asananda. 'I chanced upon a village where I saw a temple of the Buddha.'

'Yes, he had passed that way hundreds of years ago,' Vallika interrupted. 'After so many years of walking, looking towards the past, the Buddha has given me the power to see the past. The past is the greatest teacher, second only to the Buddha.'

'What did you see?'

'The Buddha came to the village during his wanderings,' Vallika continued. 'He was given food and shelter. It was the time of famine, and there was little to go around. Still, he was fed. The next day, the fields were suddenly full of rice and corn. It was a miracle. He spent seven days, teaching them his tenets. After he left, they created a shrine to him, naming him their harvest god.'

'How did he do that for the villagers?'

'He didn't. Nature did. It simply responded to the Buddha's compassion towards the hungry villagers,' Vallika said. 'If the feeling is strong enough, Nature responds to every man. The souls of man and Nature are one.'

'How did you learn that?'

'It is what you learn walking the Lost Path of the Buddha,' Vallika said. 'The Four Sightings of the Buddha are, in reality, turning points on the true path. And you have seen them all.'

Asananda was puzzled.

'The Buddha's first sight was an old man, which set him thinking about mortality,' the bhikshu said. 'When you were small, you met an old sadhu with his bull. It was the first time you realized you too would grow old. He gave you a miracle to show you that life is like a bird meant to be free. The Buddha's second sighting was of a sick man, and he felt the inevitability of pain and disease. You met Paul, and were confronted with his loss and suffering. The book set him free. The Buddha's third sighting was of a corpse. You had already been to the charnel house when the unfaithful wife was cremated. The Ganga freed her of unbearable remorse and the charnel keeper freed her soul. The fourth sighting was that of the ascetic you met in the cave, who was meditating, seeking the cause of human suffering. The holy men and women you met on the way showed you that, to be free, one had to suffer to understand the meaning of suffering. Amogh did, so did the autistic boy, Raju. Roopvati suffered as long as she lived, and her maid lived a life of a thousand regrets. The grace of the guru was always with you, and through your actions, sometimes even without you realizing it, they got their freedom from suffering.'

Asananda thought for a while.

'With suffering comes regeneration,' Vallika continued. 'That is what enlightened the Buddha, when he came to meditate under the tree at Gaya, after wandering and suffering both in body and the mind. Look at this tree under which we sit now. It's ancient. Look at some of its branches, they are struck with disease and are decaying. Some are already dry and leafless; they stand like skeletal fingers frozen in rigor mortis. Soon they will fall and rot. But look at the tree in its wisdom and entirety, see the new branches growing, the young leaves sprouting on them. It's like an ascetic that stands by this lake of knowing and meditates on the fates of those who pass beneath it.'

Asananda was overcome. He hugged Tapussa and Vallika in turn. He clasped Raag in his arms and said a prayer over her.

He touched the abbess's feet one last time. She blessed him. A thought crossed his mind.

'What was Raag's quest?'

'To become the best of guides,' said the abbess. 'On a journey, nothing is better than having a good guide. And she was.'

'Yes, indeed. She helped me discover the Lost Path of the Buddha. What do you have in mind for her next?'

'Now she has to learn how to guide herself, for that is the greatest quest of all,' the abbess said cryptically. 'It can be undertaken only on the path of the heart.'

'She has a great heart,' Asananda told the abbess, looking at his young companion affectionately. 'I'm sure you will teach her how to walk that path.'

'I will, she has more journeys ahead, while yours is nearing its end,' the abbess said. 'Go to Kedarnath now, along the Path of the Buddha. Travel beyond to the land of glaciers and endless snow, avoiding the crevices and the thundering rivers. Take the route the child yogi Neelkanth took centuries ago. Bathe in the Mansarovar lake. And walk up, through the Himalayan trails, to reach the cave and the book that awaits you.'

Asananda bowed. With tears in his eyes, he turned away from them to continue his journey.

The Monk and the Sadhu's Sandals

Asananda rode the bike all the way to Joshimath. When he reached Tapovan valley, he felt tired. He made for the famous sulphur springs. Groups of ascetics, who had left their sanctuaries in the woods, were enjoying mud baths. Asananda lay in one of the mineral pools, letting the warmth of the soothing water spread over his aching limbs, reviving him. Above, on the projecting ridge, formed by lime residues, spring water sparkled and danced. The forest was a vast, calm presence and the wind brought the heady scent of mountain flowers from distant boughs. Asananda lay still, his eyes closed, aware of the gigantic snow-brushed peaks standing afar. After his bath, he decided to leave the bike behind. Perhaps some villager would take it home. Walking up the steep mountain paths would be easier than riding the bike, passing ancient temples with their uneven stone roofs, where pilgrims have been worshipping for millennia. Only the Himalayas can host time, the monk thought. Countless centuries sleep among its milky slopes and crevices. The peaks cast their eternal shadows over vistas of glaciers, snowbound trails and caves within which ascetics seek the secret of the universe through their worship of Shiva.

'The universe has only one true secret,' Asananda remembered Gyanananda saying. 'And that is man.'

The monk continued his climb, travelling higher and higher, deviating from the Curzon trail – named after the former British Viceroy of India, an intrepid mountaineer and explorer. For days Asananda trudged on under the protection of the jagged, white peaks of the Badrinath range that lay to his north and west. He passed Chitkul, the last Indian village on the frontier, from where he bought food with the last of his money. He would not need money where he was going; if he found the cave and the Book of Shiva, nothing else mattered. If he didn't, he would simply freeze to death, and his body would be found decades later by mountaineers or trekkers, preserved in clear Himalayan ice. It was not a bad way to go, he thought, lying in the eternal womb of the sacred mountains. Even when the snow melted, which it rarely did at those heights, few bothered to remove the bodies of lost climbers, and they lay undisturbed in the company of their hardy mules.

Driven by purpose, Asananda did not feel the days pass as he travelled through high mountain passes guarded by silver oaks where rhododendrons grew thick and bright. He descended into valleys where butterflies floated in and out of bamboo thickets. He came across meadows dotted with wildflowers where trekkers had set up tents. Huge griffon vultures circled overhead, seeking food from the visitors. Old concrete bridges, their sides cracking, spanned mountain streams. The air buzzed with the babble of waterfalls. As the dusk spread, it became noticeably colder, but it did not bother Asananda. His body recalled meditating in the remote Himalayan cave he had reached after leaving the military hospital in another life, not feeling the cold that stalked the blizzard-torn mountainside. It seemed like centuries ago.

Whistles of the wind interrupted the silence. A cluster of lights shone in the distance. He hoped to find a village there where he could get shelter for the night. And maybe some warm yak's milk. He started to walk down. The first house he came across was little more than a small stone hut. Inside, he found an old man with the matted tresses of a yogi, his body smeared with ash, sitting cross-legged on a leopard skin. Asananda muttered a greeting, but the man did not reply. He was lost in contemplation. Asananda bent down to touch the holy man's feet.

'Where have I reached, Holy One?' Asananda asked. 'I hope I'm not lost.'

The ascetic's eyes opened and looked straight into his. Asananda was struck speechless. It was the face of a great ape that stared at him with dark blue eyes full of calm curiosity. With its thin red lips, smooth pink skin and great brow rimmed with silver fur, the effect was mesmeric. In its eyes, he saw soaring mountains and gigantic oceans, rivers and meadows; day circling into night as galaxies expanded and swirled. Asananda witnessed the journey of the soul as it travelled along the unchartered paths of the universe. He saw the beginning of life as a drop of water that fell from the sky into the primordial ocean. He saw the trees come to life, beasts being born and the first man taking his first steps in a timeless garden. He saw men make love, kill each other and plant saplings. The past cleared and he saw a trail submerged in snow, winding its way beneath soaring peaks, leading to a small black dot that was the sole blemish on the mountain's snowy face. The monk felt like he was being borne through the air by the power of the sadhu's gaze. The black spot revealed itself as the mouth of a snow covered cave. He recognized it as his destination. The vision ended and the sadhu disappeared.

Asananda felt weightless and disembodied. The cold flooded the hut. His extremities felt numb. He fumbled for the box of matches in his satchel. With trembling hands, he tried to light a fire, but the matches were damp. Asananda sighed. At these heights, it was common for people to slowly freeze to death. First the hands and feet would go numb. The cold would creep up through the limbs and spread slowly over the face and neck, turning into welcome warmth. The eyelashes would be encrusted with frost, as would his nostrils and lips. 'O master,' he called out to Gyanananda from the depths of his soul. 'I cannot go on. For how many more days do I walk? How far?' He closed his eyes, and saw Gyanananda's shining eyes and questioning smile. Time and the cold passed over him like a mantle being drawn in the night. Asananda dreamt that he was travelling through endless whiteness, borne by strong hands. Voices far away spoke in an unintelligible tongue. Asananda surrendered to the swaying darkness.

He woke up in a small room. He was lying on a straw pallet. A stove burned in one corner, its heat warming the room. He stood up on unsteady legs and tried to open the door. The effort left him tired. The door creaked open and a lama wearing a yellow robe came in with a bowl of gruel. Asananda took the bowl and began to eat greedily. He hadn't felt so hungry in years.

'Where am I?' he asked at the end of the meal.

'You are safe in a monastery. You were unconscious when you were brought here,' the lama said in a lilting voice.

'Who brought me?' he asked.

'The yak herders in the valley. They found you lying in the ruined hut. You were delirious. You were shouting aloud about a sadhu in the hut.'

The recollection of an ascetic who sat meditating in the darkness and seeing a vision about the universe came back to Asananda.

'Yes, I did meet a sadhu there,' Asananda said. 'But he was not an ordinary sadhu.'

'You imagined it; no one lives there. The hut is a ruin, and it has been for years. The herders say it is cursed. Perhaps you met a mountain spirit. Many of them roam the Himalayas.'

The lama was clean-shaven with dark, slanting eyes. He asked Asananda to follow him outside. They entered a large hall with giant windows outside which the Himalayas soared into a bright blue sky. An old man sat on a low stool, reading. When Asananda approached, he looked up. His eyes were bright like black berries in summer. His face was lined and kind. The tall monk bowed and left Asananda with the old man.

'Are you the master of this monastery?' Asananda asked. 'I thank you for rescuing me.'

The old man nodded. 'We do what we must,' he said.

'Where am I?' Asananda asked.

'You are at Thhuling Math,' the old master replied. 'The home of the Buddha. For someone who walks the Lost Path of the Buddha, it is only natural that you should reach me.'

'I'm looking for the Book of Shiva,' he said. 'Can you help me?'

The lama looked at him with shrewd eyes. 'This monastery lies on the road to the Kailash mountain and the Mansarovar lake, one called the road to self-discovery,' he said. 'Centuries ago, a boy monk named Neelkanth stayed here on his way to Mansarovar. Since then, all who come here walk in his footsteps. It is said that the one who finds his footprints will reach the end of his soul, freed of all karma.'

Sometime in the 1700s, an eleven-year-old boy monk named Neelkanth set out from home, seeking a place to build a hermitage. He travelled to the Himalayas, taking a perilous route full of dacoits, furious rapids and treacherous glaciers, walking along trails frozen by icy winds that stalked barren landscapes. He walked through snow, rain and blizzards, crossing the rivers Mangang, Gomal Chhu, Dongpu, Dongu and Dharma Yankti dressed in little more than a loincloth. How he did not freeze to death or wasn't killed by wolves or brigands is still a mystery.

'How does one find the footprints of Neelkanth?' asked Asananda.

'You need the right shoes,' the lama said. He clapped his hands. The young lama came in. The old man muttered something in his ear. The lama nodded and left, returning with a little wooden box, which he laid at his master's feet. The old monk opened the lid and took out a pair of worn leather sandals.

'Did these belong to Neelkanth?' Asananda asked.

'They belonged to a master,' the lama replied. 'All masters are the same, once you recognize their footprints.'

'Perhaps they belonged to you once, or to your master,' Asananda speculated.

'They belonged to a sadhu who stopped here on his way to the Kailash when my master was alive,' the lama said. 'He had spent many years meditating in a stone hut in the mountains, close to a village of herders. He left these behind.'

'When was this?' Asananda asked. The lama shrugged his frail shoulders.

'Oh, it was decades ago, at the time my master was alive,' he answered. 'I was a child when I met the sadhu for the first time. I was on my way down to the village to buy fresh milk for my master. But the sadhu doesn't live there anymore.'

Asananda shook his head, 'I met him in the stone hut below.'

The lama raised his eyebrows. 'Perhaps you did. The Himalayas are home to many strange things. Perhaps you saw your master. Or maybe it was the great Yeti you saw, the one white men refer to as the Abominable Snowman. Let me assure you, there is nothing abominable about him.'

Asananda nodded in agreement. The old lama continued, 'The one you saw was Hanuman, the First Father of men, the great silver ape who is the eleventh incarnation of Shiva,' said the lama. 'He is the greatest ascetic of all and shows himself to true seekers in many forms. To you he came as a sadhu, because yours is the way of the renunciate. You are blessed. Stay here until you recover your strength. Then the final part of your journey will begin.'

Asananda stayed at the monastery for a week, sleeping and meditating. He left one morning, slipping on the sandals the old lama gave him. The sky was the colour of a peacock's crest and sunlight glittered sharply on the landscape. He walked, stepping on rocks and mud and wading through gushing streams. He cut across small but furious mountain rivers in makeshift boats rowed by rough mountain men. A few days later, he crossed the great river Sutlej and continued his journey, taking shelter in the tents of yak herders at night. As he trudged on, Asananda felt Mount Kailash, the abode of Shiva, like a gigantic presence. It came closer with each passing day, until one evening, he saw the lights of Tarchen village shining in the distance. The monk quickened his steps, for he knew that his destination was less than a day's walk away.

In faraway Rishikesh, in his mind's eye, the owner of the sandals saw Asananda's progress in the Himalayan wilderness, turned over in his bed and smiled in his sleep.

Asananda and the Wandering Man

In Tarchen, Asananda was given shelter by a villager who shared his meagre dinner of spinach and rough bread with him. He left early in the morning, the snowy cone of Mount Kailash hovering in the distance as he topped a pass. The sandals the old lama had given him seemed to be guiding his steps. He paused at the sight of the holy mountain, which hid the cave of Shiva. Below him lay the crescent-shaped Rakshas Tal, the Lake of Demons. Beyond the enchanted water, wrapped by sunlit clouds, floated the silver peak of Kailash. He prostrated himself on the icy ground, hands folded at his forehead in obeisance to the home of the primeval god.

'I am coming home, my Lord, to the womb of stone, where I was reborn,' he whispered.

Beyond the Rakshas Tal shone the Mansarovar, its tranquil blue waters inviting the monk to immerse himself in its sanctity. Along its shore, coloured prayer flags flapped in the wind. Some were grouped together like tents while others were planted along the lakeside on wooden masts, with mounds of stones holding them in place. Birds crowded the banks; black-headed gulls wheeled around overheard, uttering cries that sounded eerily like laughs.

Water nests of crested grebes paddled in the shallows. Brahminy ducks glided in slow circles. As Asananda approached, the birds did not scatter. On the shore, in the distance, he saw a figure on the lakefront gazing out at the silver forehead of Kailash. It was Ramdhan, the storyteller, who, too, had been bound for Kailash. Asananda was glad to see his old friend.

'I'm happy you've reached,' the storyteller remarked, drawing his thick shawl around his shoulders. 'It's a long way from Rishikesh.'

Asananda nodded. 'Isn't it? So, have you bathed in the lake yet?'

'Mansarovar is the lake of stories. Did you know that Lord Brahma created it for his sons to offer prayers to Shiva? Since then every person who comes here to take a holy dip brings his or her stories to the lake, seeking happy endings. They seek a shortcut to god, but there is none. All your stories have to end first.'

'For you everything is a story, isn't it?' asked the monk.

'Isn't that true of everyone?' asked the storyteller. 'Each one of us is made up of a bunch of stories, short and long.'

'What is the moral of the story?' Asananda asked.

'Tell your story if you want to be heard. God is the listener.'

'Is he listening to you?'

'I'm an old man, tired of telling stories,' said the storyteller. 'Besides, nobody wants to hear real stories anymore. They watch television instead. I am an anachronism.'

Asananda laughed. He placed his satchel on the ground, kicked off his sandals and stripped down to his loincloth.

'Would you join me for a dip in the lake? Or have you already done so?' he asked.

The storyteller held up his hands. 'Not yet. Why don't you go ahead?'

'This is a momentous occasion, taking a dip in Mansarovar. It is one of the last stops in my long journey. They say drinking from it will take me straight to Shiva,' Asananda said, wading into the shallows, disturbing an annoyed cluster of sandpipers who took wing uttering their typical piping, three-note cries. The water was so cold that he felt it form a sheath over his bones. If he lay there too long, he would be encased in a sheet of ice, he thought. His teeth chattered as he recited the Mrityunjaya mantra, the most mystical of all of Shiva's mantras, the one with power over death and disease.

Om tryambakam yajamahe
sugandhim pusti-vardhanam,
urvarukam iva bandhanan
mrtyormuksiya mamrtat

Om, we worship the Three-Eyed One (Lord Shiva), who is fragrant and nourishes all beings. May he sever our bondage of worldly life, and thus liberate us from the fear of death by making us realize that we are never separated from our immortal nature.

Asananda waded back to the shore. His wet clothes wrapped him in a glacial embrace. He shuddered.

'If you catch a chill and die of fever, how will you find the Book of Shiva?' asked the storyteller in an amused tone.

'I will,' Asananda said with conviction. 'I've come this far. Why don't you just stick to telling stories?'

The storyteller sighed. 'I believe my time for stories is over,' he said. 'But now that I have seen you, I will tell you one last story. And I warn you. Absolutely my last.'

Asananda sat on the ground in the lotus position and asked the storyteller to begin. Now that he had come so far, he felt he had all the time in the world for an old friend.

'Just as Yama was the first man who died in this world, the first storyteller was his record keeper ...'

Yama lived in a huge mansion in the middle of the Island of Death on River Vaitarna. His mansion had many rooms. Yama's many-storeyed abode was built on a volcano. A bridge of bones connected the island to the shore. A storyteller sat at the entrance to the bridge and his task was to record details of the souls who entered Death's mansion. Each one had to write his name and story down in the book before he was allowed to pass. At the end of the day, Yama read all the stories in the book. Each soul was assigned a place in Death's mansion according to their actions. The truly exalted souls were given rooms on the top floor with huge windows and a view of the gardens, where they sat and meditated. Those who had led ordinary lives were sent to live in rooms on the ground floor, where they waited the day they would return to the world and begin life afresh. The souls of children lived in the garden filled with flowering shrubs, fruit trees, playgrounds and jungle gyms. The truly evil ones, who had committed unspeakable acts of cruelty, were sent down to the cellars where they writhed in agony as the flames of the volcano seared them endlessly. These souls would wait for centuries, sometimes millennia, before they were reborn as insects, reptiles or diseased animals. The House of Death was also called the House of Justice. Nobody could escape the storyteller or his master.

One day, many centuries ago, a set of twins was born to a rich merchant in a village. They lived in a big house with a multitude of rooms, great arched doorways, many courtyards and its own temple. Fat pink waterlilies grew in a small tarn in the far corner of the compound of the house. The twins woke up together to the sound of temple bells as their mother performed her morning prayers and went to sleep lulled by the fragrance of frangipani in the breeze. They were inseparable, playing, eating and sleeping together even as they grew up. Their mother dressed them in identical clothes and their tastes in food were similar too, and even their voice sounded the same. When they behaved badly – teasing the servants, plundering the kitchen and, when they grew up, stealing the clothes the maids left on the steps of the tarn when they bathed – their mother would scold them both. But one twin stole a few more sweets and hid the clothes of the maids so well that they couldn't find them until, taking pity on their nakedness and sobs, his kinder brother brought them out. When they saw a street dog, the first one threw stones at the animal, while his twin deliberately spoiled his own aim. In private, they would quarrel about these matters, but they soon made up, with the nasty twin promising his brother that he would never repeat his mistakes. But, of course, he would forget, and go back to his ways. Their mother would get complaints from villagers, about her boys pulling a girl's hair and making her cry, throwing stones at the mango trees in a neighbour's orchard or stealing a blind man's cane. She also heard stories of the brothers doing random acts of kindness – helping the old priest collect flowers for the evening prayer, feeding a cow that had grown too old to forage or taking a lost child home to her parents. The poor mother was very confused. She often asked them how they could be so cruel even though they could show such kindness. Only the twins knew the secret, but said nothing.

'Even I can't tell you apart, but remember that the one who does bad things should be stopped by the other,' she said. 'Or else, he will be reborn a spider or a scorpion while the good one will enjoy a comfortable afterlife.'

The twins grew into men; each continuing to live according to his nature. The bad twin spent time in gambling dens and dancing houses while his brother became a scholar. One evening the scholar sat in his library, watching the shadows lengthen outside the window. He had just finished reading a story in which a man, encountering Death in the market, went to Samarrah to escape but was taken by him anyway. The smell of sandalwood and flowers wafted in the breeze towards where the scholar sat thinking about fate, and how it was impossible to cheat death, when his twin rushed into the house with a wild look on his face.

'What happened? You look distraught,' his brother said.

'I'm taking my horse and riding off to Samarrah,' he cried. 'I had just stepped out of the tavern when I met Death. He made a nasty gesture, as if he was going to get me. I'm getting out of here.'

The scholar was deeply worried. However, he hid his feelings and reassured his brother.

'It's probably just a mad man. How do you know he was Death?'

'He told me,' said the bad brother.

The scholar laughed, but his heart was not in it. He had read the story.

'Samarrah is a day's ride from here,' he said. 'Have some tea with me before you go, for I won't know when you will return. Here, let me make you some.'

'Hurry, brother, for I've to leave immediately.'

The good twin was worried about his brother, whom he loved more than anyone else. He went inside and made tea, into which he poured a powerful sleeping draught. The bad twin drank it and slumped to the floor. The scholar lifted him and put him to bed. He called the servants to bring his horse around and rode to Samarrah. Being identical in appearance, Death could not tell the difference. He took the scholar away to the house by the lake. When the bad twin woke, he couldn't find his brother. He dismissed the thought of seeing Death outside the tavern, telling himself that he was drunk and must have been hallucinating. The next day, some citizens of Samarrah brought the scholar's body home.

Meanwhile, the scholar's soul, which had reached the bridge of bones, told the storyteller about what had happened and how he had cheated Death. Hearing this, Death was distraught. He gave the scholar's soul a place among the exalted, for his sacrifice equalled his wisdom. Then he went to meet the twin who had escaped him. He sat outside the tavern disguised as a woman. The bad twin had started drinking more because he missed his brother. When he staggered out of the tavern, Death accosted him.

'Get lost, old woman,' the drunkard shouted. 'You scared me once and I lost my brother.' Death held his forearm gently; his touch was like ice. The drunkard became suddenly sober. Death told him what his brother had done, and how he had mistaken one twin for the other.

'Take me too, for after this I can't live with myself,' cried out the distressed man. 'I want to be with my brother.'

Death shook his head.

'I can't take you twice,' he said and vanished.

The bad twin became the man who could not die, doomed to wander forever carrying the burden of the sorrow he had caused others.

'How sad,' Asananda said. 'What is the moral of your last story?'

'As we all know, all of us are two people, one good and the other evil,' said the storyteller. 'Death is the greatest guru of all, teaching us that the good may find peace in his abode while evil wanders, pursued by guilt and rage, perpetrating more evil because he cannot bear the torment he has unleashed upon himself and others. He doesn't know what else to do except cause more pain.'

'Is there no salvation for the evil?' Asananda asked. 'My master says there is salvation for everyone.'

'Perhaps, but I don't know. A sadhu I met told me this story,' the storyteller said. 'I found him sitting by the lake, staring at the water. There were tears in his eyes. He said he was tired of running and had come here to give himself to the lake, and be freed from his torment. You know, he had committed many cruel deeds. He was a murderer and a kidnapper of young children.'

The storyteller looked up, hearing Asananda's sharp intake of breath. 'Do you know him?'

Asananda did not wish to answer. He prayed Ramdhan had not recognized Puran, the man who had taken his love and life away forever. He thought he saw a soft glint of amusement pass in the storyteller's eyes, but decided against saying anymore. Ramdhan shook his head in a bemused fashion.

'When he saw me first, he looked as if he had seen a ghost,' he said. 'He just let out a terrified scream and fled at the sight of me.'

'Where did he go?'

'He ran to the lake to drown himself, but Mansarovar just wouldn't let him sink. I dragged him out eventually, and he thrashed in my grip trying to get away. He kept asking me to forgive him.'

'Why?'

'I think he was mad, or perhaps I resembled someone he once knew. I don't know. In the end, I calmed him down and he clung to me like a baby, weeping uncontrollably. I asked him to tell me about himself, but he refused. That's when he told me the story of the twins, and he said that he was a man doomed to live forever, like the evil brother in the story. He had tried to commit suicide so many times; by hanging himself from rafters of ruined buildings and wayside trees, jumping off cliffs, leaping into funeral pyres and throwing himself under the wheels of trains and buses. He was a frightening sight to behold, disfigured and ugly, blind in one eye with a deformed body and skin a mass of sores. Yet he didn't die.'

Asananda closed his eyes to keep the bitter tears from flowing.

'What happened to him?' he asked.

The storyteller gestured vaguely towards the mountains. 'He left yesterday, hoping to freeze to death, I'm sure. But the strange thing about him was that, lame as he was, he was running. I asked him why he was running and he replied that once he ran to catch someone but couldn't. After that, he has been running away from himself.'

Asananda realized that salvation can be a cruel journey, too. Death is the master of evil and Puran, seeking it, would be freed only through pain. One day, his master would find him stretched out on his back on the ice, his sightless eyes open to the sky and his cold blue skin impervious to the blizzards and snow. With absolute certainty, Asananda realized that Death would forgive Puran and it would give him release. But before that, he had to gain the forgiveness of one more.

'But why did so many people have to suffer?' Asananda asked his guru in his mind. 'Why did so many suffer in the wake of one man's lust and greed? Koyal, Ramdhan, Roopvati, the murdered boatman, Ketaki and so many nameless parents and children. Why?'

The mountains stared back at him impassively. Ramdhan touched Asananda briefly on his arm.

'Now I must bathe in the holy lake. You have to reach Kailash and circumambulate it, for that is the sacred law,' he said.

'Yes, I will. After that, I've a book to find.'

'And a story to finish. Remember, you are the story you tell.'

The storyteller stripped to his waist. His body was covered with tatoos formed by millions of words swirling in dense patterns all over his skin, making up thousands of stories. He waded into the sacred lake and shivered as the icy water rose up to his waist.

'Goodbye, my friend,' the storyteller said as the water rose to his chin and he started to sink, 'I told you my last story and I'm happy it was you who heard it. All my stories are over and finally I'm free to sleep.'

Asananda paused for a moment, arm raised to stop him.

'Wait!' he cried.

The storyteller turned towards Asananda for one last time and waved. 'Asananda, I recognized him,' he said, his words blurring in the wind as he slowly sank into the water. 'I recognized Puran, and I forgave him.'

The wind blew from the distant heights and the snowbound valleys, a gentle wind, a wind full of soothing words. He thought he heard a snatch of a lullaby, but was convinced he was mistaken. The storyteller had vanished into the lake. Asananda lowered his arm. With the name of Shiva on his lips, Asananda turned away and walked on to find the Book of Shiva.

Asananda and the Book of Shiva

The monk trudged slowly up the slope of the mountain as it rose in jagged ridges and snowy slopes. His heart raced with expectation. The air grew thin as he began his climb. The snow lay in thick white folds. In the cold, brilliant sunlight, the gigantic white peak of the Kailash sparkled. The monk stepped on rocks, pools of water and great patches of snow, skipping over little rivulets like a mountain goat. At night, he took shelter in a wayside cave and set out in the morning to begin the steep climb to Dolma Ghat. From there to Mount Kailash was a long walk, but he hoped to do it in a day. His legs felt strong and powerful in the lama's sandals.

The wind howled as it swept down from the passes, snipping at his skin. He could hear a river flowing in the distance as it took birth in the great floes of ice beyond; the harsh sounds of frozen slabs cracking felt frighteningly close. It was nearly evening when he began his ascent; he had to be careful not to be spotted by the army's snow patrols since it was forbidden to climb the Kailash. But he had to search among the great ice-covered slopes for his cave; its mouth likely hidden by a huge snowfall or jagged curtains of frost. He felt a headache coming on; drawing breath was becoming difficult. He became unaware of time; shadows of dusk flowed over swathes of snow, darkening the slopes. Above him, the Kailash's great peak glowed golden in the last of the sunlight. He had to find the cave soon or else he would be lost in the endless expanse of ice when darkness fell, and would die.

As he walked further, he suddenly felt a sense of déjà vu. The sunlight was fading. The way seemed familiar, sunk between shores of grainy snow, interrupted by puddles of blackish water that had melted and pooled in between. Snowbanks curved and tilted as the great mountain reared up above the monk. He felt small and insignificant. Suddenly he heard someone singing. He looked around but there was only the endless whiteness that stretched as far as the eye could see. The song kept coming closer. He recognized it as the song of Shiva.

> *Shiva Shambho Shambho*
> *Shiva Shambho Mahadeva*
> *Hara Hara Hara Hara Mahadeva*
> *Shiv Shambho Mahadeva*
> *Hala Hala Dhara Shambho*
> *Hey Anathha Nathha Shambho*
> *Hari Om Hari Om Hari Om Namah Shivaya ...*

The singer's voice was melodious. It soared and dipped as the names of Shiva waltzed in the air below the mountain of the Lord, as if leaving to encircle its massive girth. As he reached a curve, he met a holy man on his way down. He was small of stature and carried a stout staff. A cloth bag was slung over his shoulder. He wore nothing except a loincloth. The ascetic smiled and raised his hand in greeting. The monk had a helpless sense of being trapped in a circle.

'This has already happened,' he told himself. 'It couldn't be happening again.' The wind blew a fragment of mist that enveloped them both for an instant and then dissipated. Asananda could not recall when or where he had seen the ascetic, but he knew that he was experiencing something that had occurred a long time ago.

'Aren't you freezing?' he asked.

The holy man shrugged and asked him if he had a smoke. Asananda said he didn't smoke. The ascetic said, 'Hashish is Lord Shiva's substance. It is the smoke of other realms.'

'Maybe I will smoke when Lord Shiva takes me to those realms,' Asananda answered.

The holy man laughed at Asananda's words.

'You speak as if you've read the Book of Shiva,' Asananda said. Memory stirred again like a ghost. 'Have you read it? I'm looking for it and I've come a long way,' Asananda said. 'My master sent me on this quest.'

The ascetic's eyes twinkled merrily. He beamed. His teeth were very white against his skin, which was burned by the sun at high altitudes. He pointed a thin, long finger towards where he was coming from. 'You are nearing the end of your journey. Climb on and you will soon find a cave. On the floor, you will find a leopard skin. It would be warm to sit upon. Inside the cave is the Book of Shiva.'

'What does the book say?' Asananda asked curiously.

The ascetic laughed. 'Why don't you find out yourself?'

'How do you know about the cave and the leopard skin?'

'Because I'm coming from there. I lived there.'

'How long did you live there?'

'Maybe a hundred years. Maybe for just a few years. I don't know. It doesn't matter.'

Asananda felt he had heard the words before. He looked at the ascetic incredulously. 'You mean you are a hundred years old?'

'I don't remember.'

'Did you find Shiva after meditating in that cave?' the monk asked.

'I wasn't worthy. I was just lucky. He found me.'

'Then what happened?'

The holy man looked puzzled. 'Then nothing. I left the cave and now I am on my way to Rishikesh to find an ashram to live in, or to establish one for others to live in. There I will teach those who have been waiting for me.'

Asananda was puzzled. 'Why would they wait for you when they don't even know you?' he asked.

'They will. So will you, when the time comes,' said the ascetic preparing to walk on. 'Perhaps you already do.'

He gave a quick salute and left, leaving Asananda guessing about where he had seen him before. Soon all that was left were the fading notes of a song. Asananda walked on, puzzled by the ascetic's words. He was sure he had seen the ascetic before, but the ice dulled his senses. The evening sun cast a winged shadow on the darkening ice. Asananda looked up to see an eagle slowly circling in the pale sky; the bird's shadow glided on the snow. Sunlight sparkled on its golden wings. It swooped down, its massive wings passing overhead in a swoosh of wind and grey feathers. The eagle flew low in a straight path, as if it was inviting Asananda to follow. He followed the invisible line its flight drew on the icy ground.

A great cliff loomed ahead, swathed in snow that ran down its ridges. The eagle made straight for the cliff and Asananda thought it was going to dash against the rock. At the last moment it swerved and rose sharply, flying vertically parallel to the precipice, and came to settle on a promontory, uttering sharp, rasping cries. Asananda felt a divine purpose at work; the lama's sandals were carrying him towards his goal. A narrow path snaked its way up along the cliff face leading to a small opening that stood out starkly against the snow.

He had found the cave.

As he climbed, his steps quickened, dislodging little stones and shale. Sometimes he almost slipped. He felt the drapes of a great weariness fall over him, marking the end of a long and eventful journey. The entrance to the cave was vaguely familiar as one he had left many years ago – a long narrow tunnel that curved to the right, blocking the biting chill of snowstorms and sharp winds. His footsteps echoed in the cave's small confines. He reached its heart; a large space under an uneven arch of black, corrugated rock. At the centre, on the floor, was spread a large leopard skin. The light was poor inside; Asananda noticed a lamp beside the leopard skin. He sat on the skin and searched in his satchel for matches. A small oblong object that felt like a wooden box fell out of the bag; it was the gift Gyanananda had left behind for him with the woman who lived in the house that the merchant had built on the banks of the Nandakini.

Asananda lit the lamp and placed the object beside him on the leopard skin; he would open it later after he found the Book of Shiva. The light painted a relief of shadows on the grooves of the walls. In the glow, Asananda saw a book kept on a small folding stand in one corner of the cave. It was bound in soft tan leather, highlights glimmering in the lamplight.

'The Book of Shiva!' he shouted exultantly, reaching for the book. He carried it back to his seat, holding it close to his chest. He felt its soul permeating his body, entering his bloodstream and filling him with radiance. He was afraid it would disappear like a dream fading into the dawn. Outside the cave, a storm was swelling. A huge thunderclap. Asananda opened the cover of the book. His pulse raced. As he turned the pages one by one, a look of puzzlement slowly spread over his face. Suddenly he was seized with a great panic and began to ruffle through the pages, his urgency mounting, along with dismay and agitation. The pages were blank.

Asananda looked around wildly, hoping it was a trick played by his master to test him further. Perhaps there was another book hidden in the cave somewhere, the real Book of Shiva. The monk examined every part of the cave, shining the lamp into deep crevices and on the small ledges on the roof, crawling over every inch of the ground searching for a secret hollow; even under the leopard skin. But he found nothing. Grief possessed him, weighing him down as he collapsed on the leopard skin.

'Gyanananda, my master!' he cried out into the gloomy emptiness of the cave. 'Please enlighten me. Why do you test me so?'

The lamp suddenly flared bright. In its golden light, he noticed the box he had placed on the leopard skin. He opened its velvet wrapping. Inside it, nestled in folds of red satin, lay a pen. Its black resin gleamed in the buttery light of the lamp. 'O Narayana! What am I to do with this?' Asananda wondered aloud.

He felt its smoothness on his palm and absently rolled it between his fingers. The memories of his journey paraded like shadows flickering on the walls of the cave. The master asking him for a gift he deserved; the pomegranate tree that bloomed in blessing for a lost girl; the boy who found his guru; the sinner who found salvation in death; the sick man who found closure – these were the stories that made up his journey. All of it had a purpose, he was sure; he was missing something.

The monk realized that his travels had changed him, just as explorers encounter the unexpected and survive them. He also knew that he was no longer the man who had left the ashram by the Ganga on his master's command – he was one who had found the small god and walked the Lost Path of Buddha. The Book of Shiva was to be the final discovery, the last story in his journey.

He remembered the storyteller's last words as he bade him farewell, 'Remember, you are the story you tell. All of us, we are made of the stories we tell.'

The monk knew what he had to do. He drew the lamp closer. He placed the book back on the stand. He took the pen and unscrewed the cap. He opened the first page. On it, he wrote in elegant copperplate, 'The Book of Shiva'.

With a deep sigh, he turned the next page and started to write the first sentence of the Book of Shiva. 'On the day I was to travel to the Himalayas to find the Book of Shiva, I overslept as usual. "Narayana, Narayana!" I chanted the name of the Lord as I hurried outside to perform his ablutions. My guru Gyanananda allowed me to wake after dawn, unlike the other monks who had to rise before the brahmamuhurtham at four o'clock – the best time for meditation and worship. I had asked my master why I was allowed this indulgence. "O my son, you woke up a long time ago," my guru answered. "Only, you don't know it ..."'